THE
RACING F

QUIZ
BOOK

Volume 2

Mart Matthews

ACKNOWLEDGEMENTS

My thanks are due again to Stuart Tibber and Michelle Grainger for their able assistance with this project.

DEDICATION

This book celebrates the 25-year mark of the longest individual race sponsorship in English racing, the Ian Carnaby Stakes at Brighton every September.

It is for all the usual suspects who attend each year and for those who are no longer with us, remembering among others Pat McElroy, Stewart Parker, Richard Gibbons, and Brian and Pat Hilton.

THE RACING POST

QUIZ BOOK

1,000
QUESTIONS ON
HORSERACING

Volume 2

Mart Matthews

First published by Pitch Publishing on behalf of Racing Post, 2022

Pitch Publishing Pitch Publishing,
9 Donnington Park,
85 Birdham Road,
Chichester,
West Sussex, PO20 7AJ

www.pitchpublishing.co.uk
info@pitchpublishing.co.uk
www.racingpost.com/shop

ISBN 9781839501050

Typesetting and origination by Pitch Publishing
Printed and bound in Great Britain by TJ Books Ltd, Padstow

CONTENTS

Quiz No. 1

ALPHABET ALLEY – A

All the answers in this category are horses beginning with 'A'

1) In the 40 years up to 2021 only three horses beginning with an A have won the Grand National. Who are they?

2) Where the Queen Mother Champion Chase is concerned, he was the meat in a Moscow Flyer sandwich. Who was he?

3) Between 2013 and 2017 the Dubai World Cup was won on three occasions by horses beginning with an A. Who were they?

4) The doyen of racing commentators, Peter O'Sullevan, owned a versatile horse that, in 1974, took the Triumph Hurdle at Cheltenham and then followed up with the Chester Cup later in the same year, before completing a trio of big race wins by landing the Northumberland Plate as well. He was trained on each occasion by Cyril Mitchell. Who was he?

5) Which horse owned by JP McManus, trained by Rebecca Curtis and ridden by AP McCoy won the 2013 Albert Bartlett Novices Hurdle at Cheltenham?

6) Since Athens Wood in 1971, who is the only winner of the St Leger to begin with an A? It happened in 2010.

7) Which superb stayer under jockey Doug Smith became, in 1949, the first horse since Isonomy in 1879 to win the cup Triple Crown by winning the Ascot Gold Cup, the Goodwood Cup and the Doncaster Cup?

8) Which tremendously game chaser responded to AP McCoy's efforts to hold off all challengers and land successive Ryanair Chases for trainer Jonjo O'Neill in 2010 and 2011?

9) Which filly, trained by Noel Murless, completed the 1,000 Guineas and Oaks double in 1971?

10) In the 240-year history of the Derby and the Oaks, 2019 was the first time that the winners of both races started with an A. Who were the two horses involved?

Quiz No. 2

ALPHABET ALLEY – B

All the answers in this category are horses beginning with 'B'

1) In the 1970s the St Leger was won by three horses beginning with B. The respective jockeys were Lester Piggott, Joe Mercer and Tony Murray. Who were the three horses?

2) Which horse, trained by Martin Pipe and ridden by Peter Scudamore, won successive Welsh Grand Nationals in 1988 and 1989?

3) Which Linda Ramsden-trained speedball is the only horse to win the Epsom Dash in different centuries by doing so in 1998 and 2001?

4) Which horse did David Pipe land the Pertemps Handicap Hurdle at Cheltenham with in successive years in 2010 and 2011?

5) Not seen as much on racecourses now due to technological change, this one was very impressive in winning the 2010 Champion Hurdle for Nicky Henderson and Tony McCoy. Who was he?

6) Between 2010 and 2012 Cheltenham's Albert Bartlett Novices' Hurdle was won three times in a row by horses beginning with B. The successful trainers were Pat Gilligan, Nicky Henderson and Lucinda Russell, while the successful jockeys were Andrew Lynch, Barry Geraghty and Campbell Gillies. Who were the three horses?

7) The name of the 16-1 Jessica Harrington-trained winner of the RSA Chase at Cheltenham in 2011 references either a town in Lincolnshire or an American city. What was it called?

8) A once-popular soup that now seems to have gone out of fashion, it did however provide jockey Michael Bowlby and trainer Nicky Henderson with the Whitbread winner in 1989 with which horse?

9) Owned by Khaled Abdulla, trained by Andre Fabre and ridden by Olivier Peslier, this French filly was an extremely impressive winner of Royal Ascot's Coronation Stakes in 2001. Who was she?

10) Trained by Colm Murphy and ridden by Barry Geraghty, this horse ran out the winner of the 2010 running of the Queen Mother Champion Chase at Cheltenham. Who was it?

Quiz No. 3

ALPHABET ALLEY – C

All the answers in this category are horses beginning with 'C'

1) The second running of the Dubai World Cup in 2001 saw a win for a horse trained by Bob Baffert and ridden by Jerry Bailey that could have been named for a Liverpool footballer. What was it called?

2) Lord John Oaksey was the breeder and part-owner of the popular winner of the Hennessy at Newbury in 2011 which was trained by Mark Bradstock and ridden by Mattie Batchelor. What was its name?

3) Which horse that shares its name with a meal proved to be a hot horse for trainer Fred Armstrong when it won the Cesarewitch in 1955, the Great Metropolitan in 1956 and the Chester Cup in 1957, breaking the course record in the middle of those three races?

4) This horse, owned by JP McManus and trained by Gordon Elliott, was a standing dish at Cheltenham, winning there three years in a row; firstly, in 2015, it took the National Hunt Chase for amateur riders, then, in 2016, the Fulke Walwyn – Kim Muir Chase, and finally, in 2017, the Glenfarcas Cross-Country race. What was it called?

5) It's hard to believe that Keith Richards was ever one of these, but he was, and got to perform for the Queen, who owned this winner of the 1953 Royal Hunt Cup, trained by Cecil Boyd-Rochfort and ridden by Doug Smith. What was its name?

6) In the 1990s two winners of the Cheltenham Gold Cup had the same word in their names. This happened in 1992 and 1998, the first of them trained by Toby Balding and the second by Dino Harding. Who were the two horses?

7) Which horse gave Lester Piggott his first big winner as a trainer when, piloted by Cash Asmussen, it won Royal Ascot's Coventry Stakes in 1986?

8) Who was the 20-1 winner of the bet365 Gold Cup Chase at Sandown in 2010 for jockey Adrian Heskin and trainer Michael Hourigan?

9) Joe Mercer and Lester Piggott were the jockeys on the only two 1980s St Leger winners to begin with this letter. The years were 1981 and 1984. Which two horses were involved?

10) It sounds like a leading British bookmaker has relocated to the West Indies, but the horse, trained by John Quinn and ridden by Robert Winston, won the Epsom Dash in 2004. Who was he?

Quiz No. 4

ALPHABET ALLEY – D

All the answers in this category are horses beginning with 'D'.

1) David Pipe and Tom Scudamore combined to win the Ryanair Chase at Cheltenham in 2014 with which horse?

2) Aidan O'Brien and Johnny Murtagh took Ascot's King George two years running in 2007 and 2008 with which two Coolmore horses?

3) Between 1986 and 1988 three horses in a row beginning with D won the 2,000 Guineas at Newmarket. They were trained by Guy Harwood, Richard Hannon and Michael Stoute. Who were they?

4) Bryan Cooper was aboard when Gordon Elliott broke his duck in the Cheltenham Gold Cup on which horse in the 2016 edition of the race?

5) Nice on a trifle unless the health police have banned it by now, it also won the Lincoln in 1971 for trainer Bill Elsey and jockey Eddie Hide. What was it called?

6) An impressive winner of Cheltenham's Champion Bumper in 2009, this Phil Fenton-trained horse didn't quite live up to expectations after that. What was its name?

7) Which colt landed the 2,000 Guineas at Newmarket for Jim Bolger and Kevin Manning in 2013?

8) Which Willie Mullins-trained horse was successful at Cheltenham two years running, firstly taking the Supreme Novices' Hurdle in 2015, and following up with the 2016 Arkle Chase?

9) Father and son Aidan and Joseph O'Brien teamed up to produce the winner of York's Group One International Stakes in 2013 with a horse that has a link to September of 1939. What was it called?

10) Nine horses have won the Queen Mother Champion Chase in successive seasons since its inception in 1959, but which horse, trained by Bob Turnell and ridden by Frank Nash, was the first to do so in 1967 and 1968?

Quiz No. 5

ALPHABET ALLEY – E

All the answers in this category are horses beginning with 'E'

1) Which horse, who won the 1997 2,000 Guineas for Michael Stoute and Mick Kinane and was installed the 4-6 favourite for the Derby, could finish only fourth at Epsom?

2) This filly was the only winning Oaks ride for Richard Hills when it triumphed in 2005. What was she called?

3) When this Godolphin colt under Mickael Barzalona won the 2012 St Leger it foiled Camelot's bid for the Triple Crown. What was its name?

4) The only 1990s favourite to win the Derby was ridden by Willie Carson in 1994. What was it called?

5) He probably wasn't named for a famous blues guitarist, but he was successful in the 1972 renewal of the Chester Cup at 22-1. Who was he?

6) One of these often ends up at Gretna Green. It also won Royal Ascot's Hardwicke Stakes for Noel Murless and Lester Piggott in 1955. What was it called?

7) Which horse is the only one to win the Arc at both Chantilly and Longchamp?

8) Lester Piggott's seventh Derby winner came in 1976, trained in France by Maurice Zilber. What was it called?

9) This cigarette took the 1997 Cheveley Park for Keiren Fallon and David Loder. What was its name?

10) The 2000 running of Cheltenham's Queen Mother Champion Chase produced arguably the greatest race in its history when Tony McCoy and Norman Williamson fought out the finish. Williamson, on Direct Route, lost the race by the narrowest of margins to which horse?

Quiz No. 6

ALPHABET ALLEY – F

All the answers in this category are horses beginning with 'F'

1) This winner of the Imperial Cup at Sandown in 1979, ridden by Tim Thomson-Jones and trained by Alf Smith, sounds like Henry Kissinger's dubious role on the world stage around the same time. What was it called?

2) This horse, winner of a Coventry Stakes, an Eclipse and two Champion Stakes in the late 1920s is something golfers are always pleased to hit off the tee. What was its name?

3) Bryony Frost rode and Paul Nicholls trained this popular winner of the Ryanair Chase at the 2019 Cheltenham Festival. Which horse won the race?

4) A horse called Boxer won the 1971 Triumph Hurdle at Cheltenham, and 14 years later something a boxer is likely to feel very nervous about also won the Triumph Hurdle, ridden by Steve Smith-Eccles and trained by Nicky Henderson. What was it called?

5) Which horse was an odds-on winner of the Champion Hurdle for Willie Mullins and Ruby Walsh in 2015?

6) When this horse won the first peacetime Ebor of 1946 this dance was obviously very popular. What was its name?

7) Clearly Ryan Moore and Aidan O'Brien found a way to land the 2016 Arc. With which horse?

8) Mrs Mirabelle Topham's organisation of the TV commentary of the 1950 Grand National is an amazing watch. Which horse, trained by Robert Renton and piloted by Jimmy Power, was successful in the race?

9) This old fashioned word for a mugger won the Arkle at the Cheltenham Festival of 2018 for Ruby Walsh and Willie Mullins. What was its name?

10) Which filly won the Oaks at Epsom in 2018 for jockey Donnacha O'Brien and his father Aidan?

Quiz No. 7

ALPHABET ALLEY – G

All the answers in this category are horses beginning with 'G'

1) Which horse, owned and trained by Frank Gilman, gave amateur Dick Saunders the experience of being the oldest jockey to win the Grand National in 1982?

2) The 2009 running of the 1,000 Guineas produced an unusual outcome in that the 20-1 winner, trained by Barry Hills and ridden by his son, Richard, was having its first run on turf. What was she called?

3) Which horse gave John Gosden his first Arc in 2015 after warming up for the race by winning the Derby?

4) Michael Stoute and Kieren Fallon combined to win the 2,000 Guineas in 2001 and Ascot's King George the following season with which horse?

5) Which horse that shares its name with a Caribbean racetrack won the Cheltenham Gold Cup and came second in the Grand National in 1991, on both occasions trained by Jenny Pitman and ridden by her son Mark?

6) Which filly, in 1972, gave jockey Tony Murray and trainer Ryan Price their only Oaks success at Epsom?

7) The winner of the 2013 renewal of the Henry II Stakes at Sandown was ridden by Olivier Peslier and was the title of a Billie Holiday song from 1941 that received a radio ban because it was feared that its depressing lyrics could induce suicide! What was the horse called?

8) This colt registered Vincent O'Brien's final Derby success when, under Pat Eddery, he ran out the winner of the 1982 edition of Epsom's famous showpiece. What was his name?

9) Something that anthropologists sometimes do won the 2009 running of the Cheltenham Festival opener, the Supreme Novices' Hurdle, its connections being trainer Noel Meade and jockey Paul Carberry. What was it called?

10) Paul Cole trained and Alan Munro rode the only horse beginning with this letter to win the Derby in the 1990s when it triumphed in 1991. Who was it?

Quiz No. 8

ALPHABET ALLEY – H

All the answers in this category are horses beginning with 'H'

1) A Lake District mountain pops up at Royal Ascot to give Ted Durcan and Bryan Smart a nice result in the Coventry Stakes of 2006. What was it called?

2) Willie Carson won the 2,000 Guineas four times on Don't Forget Me, Known Fact, Nashwan and his first winner in the race for trainer Bernard Van Cutsem in 1972. What was the horse called?

3) Which two colts who won the race in 2004 and 2008 are the only two this century to win the 2,000 Guineas at Newmarket starting with the letter H?

4) Which horse won Ascot's King George in 2010 for trainer Michael Stoute and jockey Olivier Peslier?

5) The jockeys on the only two fillies to win the 1,000 Guineas in the 1990s starting with H were Walter Swinburn in 1992 and Richard Hills in 1995. What were the two fillies called?

6) Excellent in a roast-beef sandwich, it also took the Northumberland Plate at Newcastle in 1963 for trainer Freddie Maxwell and jockey Peter Robinson. What was its name?

7) This exciting colt trained by Aidan O'Brien won the Irish Derby and the Arc in 2005 and Ascot's King George the following year. Who was he?

8) The year 2000 saw an English raid on the French Derby when it was won by a colt ridden by Philip Robinson and trained by Michael Jarvis that shares its name with a poem by Clive James. What was it called?

9) Which superb horse, in 1995 and 1996, won two Eclipse Stakes at Sandown and two Internationals at York?

10) Successive winners of the Epsom Dash in 2007 and 2008 began with the letter H. The first was trained by Stuart Williams and ridden by Saleem Golam, and the second was trained by Andrew Balding and ridden by William Buick. Who were the two horses?

Quiz No. 9

ALPHABET ALLEY – I

All the answers in this category are horses beginning with 'I'

1) Jockey John Reid experienced a 19-year gap between his two winning rides in Ascot's King George. Which horse, trained by Fulke Johnson-Houghton, was under him when he won it for the first time in 1978?

2) The last 20th-century winner of the 2,000 Guineas was which colt trained by Saaed bin Suroor and ridden by Frankie Dettori?

3) A beautiful ride from Gerald Mosse saw this impressive filly trained in France by Robert Collet take Royal Ascot's Coronation Stakes in 2011. Who was she?

4) How can we be sure that this horse won Newcastle's Fighting Fifth Hurdle under Bryan Cooper for trainer Henry De Bromhead in 2015? It might have been an impostor!

5) Flat maestro Aidan O'Brien turned his hand to hurdling in 2017 when he landed the Triumph Hurdle at Cheltenham with a horse that sounds like it came from Russia. What was it called?

6) One for the more mature among you! In the 1950s whenever TV coverage broke down or there was a spot of dead air they put a big card on the screen with one word on it, accompanied by what was deemed as appropriately soothing music. That word on the screen won the 1976 Cambridgeshire and its connections were Michael Stoute and Greville Starkey. What was its name?

7) Conor O'Dwyer, riding for Fergie Sutherland, won the 1996 edition of the Cheltenham Gold Cup with which horse?

8) We've already had one Billie Holiday song, and now we have another, this time it was the winner of the 2001 Cambridgeshire when James Given and Mickey Fenton joined forces at 33-1. What was the horse called?

9) Which American state was successful in the 2017 running of Royal Ascot's Hardwicke Stakes for Aidan O'Brien and Seamie Heffernan?

10) A theatrical expression was the French winner of Epsom's Coronation Cup in 1990, trained by Andre Fabre and piloted by Cash Asmussen. What was it called?

Quiz No. 10

ALPHABET ALLEY – J

All the answers in this category are horses beginning with 'J'

1) Trained by Peter Beaumont and ridden by Mark Dwyer, the 1993 Cheltenham Gold Cup winner constituted the only occasion that the race was won by a horse beginning with this letter. Who won it?

2) You could win at poker with this hand but the odds are against it. The odds, at 16-1, were against it winning Sandown's Betfred Gold Cup Chase in 2005 but, trained by Ted Walsh and ridden by Garrett Cotter, it defied those odds. What was it called?

3) Which famous Italian football club did the business in the 1883 Gimcrack at York?

4) Fred Winter's first success in the Grand National as a trainer came in 1965 when a combination of a bird and a US President got the job done. What was it called?

5) Dave Ashforth backed this 1978 St Leger winner ante-post at 66-1. On the day, the horse, trained by Clive Brittain and ridden by Eddie Hide, was returned at 28-1, going on early and leaving the field all at sea! Who was he?

6) Tony Soprano's uncle was victorious in the 2010 renewal of the Ascot Stakes, ably assisted by David Pipe and Seb Sanders. Who was he?

7) 116 years before Liverpool's first European Cup success in Rome in 1977 their left-back that night won the Northumberland Plate. What was the horse called?

8) Improving astronomically between 1983 and 1985 Clive Brittain's charge, twice piloted by Lester Piggott and once by Greville Starkey, won an Ebor at York, a John Porter Stakes at Newbury and a Hardwicke Stakes at Royal Ascot. Who was he?

9) These three are all Jimmys. The first won the Ayr Gold Cup in 2009, the second took the Hungerford Stakes in both 1968 and 1969 and the QEII in the latter year, while the third won the Stewards' Cup in 1976. Who are the three horses?

10) Cheltenham's cross-country race has been a target over the years of Irish trainer Enda Bolger. After a six year lean period he returned to the winners' enclosure courtesy of Nina Carberry and which horse in 2016?

Quiz No. 11

ALPHABET ALLEY – K

All the answers in this category are horses beginning with 'K'

1) Which Scottish football club won Royal Ascot's Queen Alexandra Stakes in 1901?

2) 1982 was a good year for this Guy Harwood trained colt when, under Greville Starkey, he won the Eclipse at Sandown before defeating Irish favourite Assert in Ascot's King George. What was his name?

3) Which area of north London known for its Irish connections was successful in the Welsh Grand National of 1966?

4) An early example of a jumps trainer targeting flat handicaps came when Jimmy Fitzgerald saddled the winner of the 1985 Cesarewitch with help from Tony Murray with which horse that sounds like three letters in a row?

5) Under Fergal Lynch, this colt, trained by Michael Stoute, beat just three rivals to win Chester's Dee Stakes in 2003 at 20-1. Then, this time with Kieren Fallon, it landed the Derby at Epsom a few weeks later. What was its name?

6) Michael Beary trained jockey Scobie Breasley's only winner of the 2,000 Guineas in 1951 with which colt?

7) Two monarchs were successful in the Lincoln inside three years when the first, partnered by Geoff Baxter and Bill Wightman, took the honours in 1980, to be followed in 1982 by another, piloted by Bryan Crossley and trained by Philip Mitchell. What were the two horses called?

8) With which horse did Luca Cumani and Ray Cochrane combine to produce the Epsom Derby winner of 1988?

9) Hereford trainer Venetia Williams landed the Pertemps Handicap Hurdle in 2009 when Aidan Coleman drove which horse to victory up the Cheltenham hill?

10) In the over 50 years since this horse won the Royal Hunt Cup in 1969
with Lester Piggott up, no other horse beginning with this letter has
won the race. What was its name?

Quiz No. 12

ALPHABET ALLEY – L

All the answers in this category are horses beginning with 'L'

1) Which Cumbrian tourist attraction, trained by Geoff Lewis and ridden by Pat Eddery, won Newmarket's July Cup in 1995?

2) In 2016 a new race was inaugurated at Cheltenham called the Dawn Run Mares Novices' Hurdle. With which three mares did trainer Willie Mullins win its first three runnings?

3) Which nautical conveyance proved extremely useful for Dick Hern and Willie Carson in the 1986 Ascot Gold Cup?

4) Willie Mullins and Seamie Heffernan combined to take the 2018 Cesarewitch on a horse who sometimes causes fences and hurdles to be omitted in races. What was it called?

5) Without the existence of Mill Reef, this colt, trained by Peter Walwyn and ridden by Duncan Keith, would have won the 1971 Derby. Who was he?

6) Which American city associated with the TV programme *Pawn Stars* won the first post-war November Handicap with jockey Harry Wragg at 20-1 in 1946?

7) Since Larkspur won the Derby in 1962 there has been just one winner of the Epsom classic to start with the letter L. Who was it?

8) Tim Forster and Toby Balding trained the only two Grand National winners of the 1980s to start with this letter. They came in 1985 and 1989. Who were they?

9) Which French port was successful for jockey CP Lemaire and trainer Jean-Claude Rouget in the French Derby of 2009?

10) It was appropriate that this actress had a racehorse named after her because she was a racehorse owner herself. The filly in question did her proud when winning the Coronation Stakes at Royal Ascot in 2010 for Johnny Murtagh and Aidan O'Brien. What was she called?

Quiz No. 13

ALPHABET ALLEY – M

All the answers in this category are horses beginning with 'M'

1) Which Mozart opera was music to the ears of Noel Murless and Geoff Lewis when they won Royal Ascot's Coronation Stakes in 1971?

2) Which 21st-century Manchester United player won the 1960 2,000 Guineas, trained by Paddy Prendergast and ridden by Ron Hutchinson?

3) Michael Dods and Paul Mulrennan were the successful combination when which speedball took back-to-back Nunthorpes at York in 2015 and 2016?

4) You would have been wise to back this horse, which was a seaside resort and one half of a comedy duo, because amongst other successes, it won the 1957 Ebor and the 1958 Cesarewitch for Sam Hall and Joe Sime. What was its name?

5) The winner of the 2018 running of the Fulke Walwyn-Kim Muir Handicap Chase at Cheltenham, trained by Warren Greatrex and ridden by Noel McParlan, is not a phrase you want to hear when travelling in an aeroplane, or, less worryingly, playing golf! What was it called?

6) In the last year of the 20th century this superb colt, trained by John Hammond and ridden by Cash Asmussen, hoovered up the French and Irish Derbies and the Arc. Who was he?

7) David Pipe and Tom Scudamore were the connections when which horse provided them with Cheltenham's Champion Bumper in 2015?

8) If it hadn't been for the existence of the mighty Arkle, this horse might have been seen as the chaser of the 60s. Trained by Fulke Walwyn and piloted by Willie Robinson, he won the Cheltenham Gold Cup of 1963 before Arkle's domination. Who was he?

9) A horse trained by Alec Stewart showed tremendous improvement and eventually became the first horse to win successive Eclipse Stakes in 60 years when taking the 1987 and 1988 editions of the race at Sandown under Michael Roberts. He also won the King George and was an unlucky second in the Arc. Who was he?

10) Which two 'Misters' have won the Grand National post-war in the 20th century?

Quiz No. 14

ALPHABET ALLEY – N

All the answers in this category are horses beginning with 'N'

1) John Reid's sole St Leger success as a jockey came aboard which Aidan O'Brien-trained colt in 1998?

2) This football club won the 1859 running of the Doncaster Cup. In the last 50 years they've sadly won nothing else! Who won that race?

3) Which horse, ridden by Andre Pommier and trained by Francois Doumen, stood between Desert Orchid and five successive wins in Kempton's King George by taking that race in 1987?

4) The 1916 Middle Park Stakes winner is a useful guide if you're out at night without a compass. What was it called?

5) Which French confectionery that can play havoc with your teeth won the 1976 Imperial Cup at Sandown for trainer Josh Gifford and jockey Gerry Enright?

6) The 1970s produced three 2,000 Guineas winners that started with N. The years involved were 1970, 1974 and 1977. Who were the three colts?

7) Piloted by Paddy Flood for trainer Tom Taaffe, this winner of the Coral Cup at Cheltenham in 2009 sounds like added-on time beckons! What was it called?

8) It's what every batsman wants to hear after an appeal, and it also won the 1871 Ebor. What was it called?

9) Tony McCoy and Paul Nolan combined to land the JLT Novices Chase at Cheltenham in 2011 with which horse?

10) Ridden by Johnny Murtagh and trained in Germany by Andreas Wohler, this winner of the 2013 running of Ascot's King George brings Charles Dickens or Jane Austen to mind, although it's a shame about the spelling! What was its name?

Quiz No. 15

ALPHABET ALLEY – O

All the answers in this category are horses beginning with 'O'

1) There were contrasting prices between the only horse beginning with O to win the 1,000 Guineas in the 1970s and the only one to do so in the 1980s. The first won in 1979 at evens under Joe Mercer, while the second won in 1982 as a 33-1 shot under John Reid. Who were the two fillies?

2) This horse was an electrifying winner of the 2013 Triumph Hurdle and seemed to have the world at his feet, but, on a terrible day at Cheltenham the following year, he was sadly killed in the Champion Hurdle. Trained in Ireland by Dessie Hughes, what was his name?

3) A clever ride by Kevin Darley and good tactics from John Gosden kept this horse well away from a head-to-head with Giants Causeway in the 2000 renewal of Ascot's QEII and brought them victory in the race. Who was the successful horse?

4) Which horse, trained by Enda Bolger and ridden by Nina Carberry, won Cheltenham's Foxhunters Chase in both 2015 and 2016?

5) The first winner of the King Edward VII Stakes at Royal Ascot after World War One in 1919 sounds like the police had a hand in his success. Which horse won the race?

6) The winner of Ascot's QEII Stakes in 2013, trained by Richard Hannon Senior and ridden by Richard Hughes, is something that has been experienced by Daley Thompson, Victoria Pendleton, Seb Coe, Jessica Ennis and Steve Redgrave, amongst others. What was it called?

7) This phenomenal filly brought great pride and satisfaction to Henry Cecil and Steve Cauthen when she took the Triple Crown in 1985, the first filly since Meld to do so. Who was she?

8) There's one of these in Covent Garden, but it obviously turned up at Ascot in 1993 to land the King George for those two Michaels, Roberts and Stoute. What was it called?

9) Geoff Wragg trained this sprinter who, in 1994, won the Cork and Orrery at Royal Ascot under Michael Hills, before adding the July Cup the next month, this time partnered by Paul Eddery. Who was he?

10) Trainer Colin Tizzard and jockey Steven Clements won the 2011 Johnny Henderson Grand Annual at Cheltenham with a horse whose name suggests a bird of prey, and it certainly flew up the Cheltenham hill for them that day! What was its name?

Quiz No. 16

ALPHABET ALLEY – P

All the answers in this category are horses beginning with 'P'

1) Cheltenham Gold Cup day of 2019 opened with a 20-1 winner of the Triumph Hurdle for Nicky Henderson and Nico De Boinville with which horse?

2) Which horse, trained by Michael Stoute and ridden by Mick Kinane, beat Derby winner Benny the Dip and 1,000 Guineas winner Bosra Sham in taking Sandown's Eclipse Stakes in 1997?

3) Which much-loved racehorse thrilled the Boxing Day crowds at Kempton when landing back-to-back King George VI Chases, trained by Fred Winter and ridden by Richard Pitman, in 1972 and 1973?

4) Trained by Ted Leader and ridden by Eph Smith, this horse completed a trio of wins in the Goodwood Stakes between 1958 and 1960, producing a new Derby trial at the course named in his honour. Who was he?

5) Add one letter to this Barry Hills-trained winner of two Goodwood Cups and a Chester Vase in the 1970s and you produce a book of the bible. What was it called?

6) In this century three horses starting with this letter have been successful in what used to be the Whitbread at Sandown. Danny Howard, Timmy Murphy and Tom Cannon rode them in 2004, 2011 and 2021. Which three horses were involved?

7) Sired by the brilliant Petingo, which horse in 1984 completed a superb sprint treble when winning the Wokingham, the Stewards' Cup and the Haydock Sprint Cup, bringing much satisfaction no doubt to Michael Jarvis and Bruce Raymond?

8) Which current-affairs television programme won the 1938 running of the Coventry Stakes at Royal Ascot at the prohibitive price of 2-9?

9) Which horse, trained by Harry Wragg and ridden by Roger Poincelet, was, at 66-1, the biggest-priced post-war winner of the Derby when it won the 1961 edition of the race?

10) Salisbury, 5 September 2002, three races to go, the first over 1m6f. In the paddock one horse stops and paws the ground in front of us. My son, Dan, puts his last £40 on him at 11-4. He leads, is challenged on both sides, headed, fights back. At the line the three cannot be separated. The photo takes forever before he's announced the winner by two short heads. With his newly recharged pot, Dan then lands Wind Chime at 6-1 and Miss Damask at 16-1 in the last two races and leaves the course over £500 better off! This wonderful battler transformed the fortunes of so many punters over so many years. Who was he?

Quiz No. 17

ALPHABET ALLEY – Q

All the answers in this category are horses beginning with 'Q'

1) Which horse provided trainer Ryan Jarvis and jockey 'Taffy' Thomas with a Lincoln winner at 28-1 in 1974?

2) Winning the Derby with this horse got trainer Roger Charlton some early kudos after taking over Jeremy Tree's Beckhampton yard. Which colt was appropriately named in the circumstances?

3) Ridden by Pat Taaffe, which horse provided the last of an amazing treble of Grand National winners for Vincent O'Brien in 1955?

4) Horses trained by Aidan O'Brien don't often go off at 50-1, but this one did when it was victorious in the 2015 Epsom Oaks under Conor O'Donoghue. What was her name?

5) Eighty years earlier, another Q had won the Oaks, alongside triumphs in an Ormonde Stakes, an Ascot Gold Cup and two Jockey Club Cups. This 1935 winner is what sometimes happens to charges brought against an individual. What was that Oaks winner called?

6) Which horse won the bet365 Gold Cup Chase at Sandown for Andrew Tinkler and Henry Daly in 2013?

7) Trainer Harry Bell, a somewhat controversial character, kept the Scottish National trophy on home soil by wining it in 1972 with Maurice Barnes on top, the first of three wins in the race for the trainer. It's what you want when you ask for a quote! What was it called?

8) Which horse, trained by Paul Nicholls and steered to victory by Nick Scholfield, took the 2015 running of the Boodles Juvenile Novices' Handicap Hurdle, commonly known as the 'Fred Winter' at Cheltenham?

9) Northern jockey Alec Russell came south to net the winner of the 1957 renewal of the Sussex Stakes at Goodwood, which you need to open a meeting. What was it called?

10) Winner of ten of her 11 races, she was also the first filly to win both the Oaks and the St Leger when successful in 1835. Ivanka probably calls herself what?

Quiz No. 18

ALPHABET ALLEY – R

All the answers in this category are horses beginning with 'R'

1) A comfortable winner of the 1963 Epsom Derby, trained by Francois Mathet and ridden by Yves Saint Martin, this French colt had to survive a doping enquiry after the race before his victory was confirmed. Who was he?

2) Which horse gave John Gosden and Jimmy Fortune success in the 2007 Royal Hunt Cup at Ascot?

3) A British win in the OLBG Mares' Hurdle at Cheltenham in 2019 with Dan Skelton doing the training and Harry Skelton the steering. On which mare?

4) With Ryan Moore in the saddle, Aidan O'Brien landed Chester's Dee Stakes for the seventh time in 2018 with the help of which famous Russian cellist?

5) In 1967 and 1968 Lester Piggott won back-to-back Irish Derbies for trainer Fulke Johnson-Houghton with two similarly named offspring of champion racehorse Ribot. What were the two horses called?

6) In 2003 Pat Smullen and Dermot Weld teamed up to take the 2,000 Guineas at Newmarket on a colt that lived up to his name that day. What was he called?

7) This horse, ridden by Philip Robinson and trained by Michael Jarvis, was a bit crazy and went to the post for the 2005 Lockinge Stakes at Newbury like a scalded cat! He came back like one too and nothing could live with him. Who was responsible for this devastating performance?

8) There's one in London and another in Guildford, and another won the Ryanair Chase at Cheltenham with Barry Geraghty and Nicky Henderson also involved in 2012. What name are we looking for here?

9) Andre Fabre was training his seventh winner of the Arc when Stephane Pasquier steered this one home at Longchamp in October 2006. Clapham Junction springs to mind when thinking about the winner. What was his name?

10) Johnny Murtagh proclaimed him the best horse he had sat on but he suffered from the brilliance of Sea the Stars. However, Aidan O'Brien's colt won the 2009 Eclipse and York's International Stakes the following year after which he deserved a nice long sleep! Who was he?

Quiz No. 19

ALPHABET ALLEY – S

All the answers in this category are horses beginning with 'S'

1) This horse's name was certainly a useful attribute to have when it was successful in the 2014 edition of the Kim Muir Chase at Cheltenham for trainer Jim Culloty and jockey Robert McNamara. What was it called?

2) There was a family feel in Cheltenham's Foxhunters Chase in 2012 and again in 2013 when which horse won back-to-back events for trainer Roger and jockey Colman Sweeney?

3) Between 1990 and 1992 jockeys Gerald Mosse, Cash Asmussen and Thierry Jarnet won the Arc on three horses beginning with S. Who were they?

4) What is usually called at half past six in a Test match won the 1826 Goodwood Cup. What was its name?

5) Unfortunately, this great racehorse met an untimely end and then, to add insult to injury, his name was attached to a pointless exercise that is held at Ascot every August. Who was he?

6) Godolphin colt Noverre was supposed to win the 2001 running of Ascot's QEII with Richard Hills acting as the role of pacemaker on another of their horses. The horse in question clearly hadn't read the script and never looked like being headed. Which horse took the prize at 33-1?

7) Which Barry Hills-trained horse won the last Royal Ascot Hunt Cup of the 20th century so easily under Neil Pollard that he became difficult to place in future races?

8) This horse, trained by Rod Millman and ridden by Alan Munro, just kept on improving through 2005 and achieved a magnificent trio of wins in the top staying handicaps, taking the Northumberland Plate, the Ebor and the Cesarewitch. Who was he?

9) Unusually for a filly, after having done the 1,000 Guineas and Oaks double in 1990 with the assistance of John Dunlop and Willie Carson, she had a crack at the colts in the Irish Derby, and they couldn't stop her either. Some filly this! Who was she?

10) Better known for his 'touches' in sprint handicaps, trainer Reg Akehurst booked Olivier Peslier to ride this horse for him in the Ascot Stakes stayers' handicap of 1996. It didn't disappoint, perhaps because of the energy generated by a name that sounds like an electricity company. What was it?

Quiz No. 20

ALPHABET ALLEY – T

All the answers in this category are horses beginning with 'T'

1) Firstly under Gary Hind and then under Jimmy Fortune, which Peter Harris-trained horse won the Epsom Dash in 1996 and again in 1999?

2) I'm sure he cost rather more than that, but he won the 2019 July Cup at Newmarket nicely enough for Ryan Moore and Aidan O'Brien. Who was he?

3) Which horse gave trainer Pat Hughes and jockey Willie Carson the Wokingham winner at Royal Ascot in 1985 with a little help from Dr Who?

4) The Arcs of 1987 and 1988 were won on which colts beginning with T by Pat Eddery and John Reid respectively?

5) Christophe Soumillon took back-to-back Dubai World Cups in 2018 and 2019 on the conjunction of two weather conditions. What was the winning horse called?

6) This Trevor Hemmings-owned horse, trained by Nicky Henderson and ridden by Mick Fitzgerald, captured the RSA Chase in 2005 at Cheltenham before turning in a superb weight carrying performance to win the Hennessy as well. Injury denied him the very real chance of a Gold Cup win the following season. Who was he?

7) Which lovely filly of Henry Candy's won the Oaks and the Champion Stakes in 1982, the King George in 1983 and the Coronation Cup in 1984?

8) Television presenter and racing journalist Julian Wilson had some success as the owner of which 1977 Gimcrack winner trained by Bruce Hobbs and ridden by Geoff Lewis?

9) JT McNamara and Rebecca Curtis teamed up to land the 2012 National Hunt Chase at Cheltenham with a horse that's added an extra person to an old song. What was it called?

10) Critics of Ascot's 2005 redevelopment suggested that you might need one of these to see this winner of the Hardwicke Stakes in 2014 for Michael Stoute and Ryan Moore! What was the horse's name?

Quiz No. 21

ALPHABET ALLEY – U

All the answers in this category are horses beginning with 'U'

1) Which Aidan O'Brien-trained colt ridden by Ryan Moore left the rest all at sea when setting the standard in the 2018 July Cup at Newmarket?

2) This filly, trained by Clive Brittain, gave jockey George Duffield the Oaks and St Leger double in 1992. What was her name?

3) Which horse won the Whitbread at Sandown for Howard Johnson and Charlie Swan in 1994?

4) Which region of Italy took the 1879 Ayr Gold Cup?

5) You don't get too many 40-1 Nicky Henderson winners at the Cheltenham Festival, but this one did the business with Jeremiah McGrath in the 2012 Fred Winter Juvenile Novices Handicap Hurdle. What was its name?

6) Trainer Jean Lesbordes and jockey Eric Saint-Martin were successful in the 1993 Arc with which horse?

7) In order to start a cricket match you need the winner of the 1876 Irish Derby. What was it?

8) Tony McCoy and Alan King sprang a 16-1 surprise with this horse owned by JP McManus in the 2015 Ryanair Chase at Cheltenham. Name please?

9) In the late 1980s this horse won the Chester Vase, the Prince of Wales Stakes, the John Porter Stakes and the Jockey Club Cup. Owned by Hamdan Al Maktoum, trained by Dick Hern and ridden by Willie Carson, what was his name?

10) With which horse did David Pipe and Tom Scudamore land a Cheltenham Festival double in 2016 and 2017 in the Ultima Handicap Chase?

Quiz No. 22

ALPHABET ALLEY – V

All the answers in this category are horses beginning with 'V'

1) The Cheltenham OLBG Mares Hurdle went to trainer Willie Mullins for an incredible eighth time in a row in 2016 when Ruby Walsh steered which mare to victory?

2) Troy and this horse are the only two four-letter winners of Ascot's King George. The year was 1955 and his French connections had nothing to do with Gene Hackman! They were Alec Head and Roger Poincelet. Who was the horse?

3) Dennis McKay rode and Doug Smith trained this winner of the 1970 Wokingham at Royal Ascot, who sounds like a young guy from one of America's southern states. Who was he?

4) When asked on his deathbed to renounce the devil this French philosopher said it was no time to be making new enemies! He also won the Doncaster Cup in 1829. What was his name?

5) Between 2014 and 2016, which Willie Mullins-trained horse won a different race at the Cheltenham Festival three years running? The events were the Supreme Novices Hurdle, the JLT Novices Hurdle and the Ryanair.

6) Which horse that was a real favourite with the Irish in general and Dermot Weld in particular won an unprecedented four Irish St Legers in a row under Pat Smullen between 2001 and 2004?

7) Peter Walwyn and Pat Eddery combined to take the 1976 Champion Stakes at Newmarket with which horse?

8) This excellent French horse took their Derby in 2008, trained by Eric Libaud, before landing the Prince of Wales Stakes at Royal Ascot the following year, with a Hong Kong Cup thrown in for good measure. Who was he?

9) A horse called Truth won the 1851 Cambridgeshire at Newmarket. Thirty-seven years later, in 1888, another word meaning 'truth' was also successful in the race. What was it called?

10) 'Chocolate' Thornton's only win as a jockey in the Queen Mother Champion Chase came aboard which Alan King-trained horse in 2007?

Quiz No. 23

ALPHABET ALLEY – W

All the answers in this category are horses beginning with 'W'

1) Trainer Bill Marshall and jockey Geoff Lewis combined to win the 1974 running of Royal Ascot's Coventry Stakes with a horse that in today's world would not be allowed to be called by this name. What was it called?

2) Which colt won the Eclipse at Sandown for Henry Cecil and Lester Piggott in 1969?

3) Perhaps Ray Davies spent some time contemplating this winner of Royal Ascot's Norfolk Stakes in 2015 for Ryan Moore and Aidan O'Brien. What was it called?

4) Another recent winner of the Norfolk Stakes was this colt trained by Peter Chapple-Hyam and ridden by Jimmy Fortune, who took the prize in 2007. He also won the July Stakes at Newmarket in that year and went undefeated as a two-year-old, although he never won again. What was his name?

5) This horse was runner-up in the 2002 Grand National when ridden by Richard Johnson and, a year earlier, he had gone one better by winning the Hennessy under Paul Flynn. However, he stays in my mind for winning the Coral Cup at Cheltenham in 2000 in the most exciting finish to any race I've ever witnessed. If you haven't seen it, watch it on YouTube and be amazed! Oh, by the way, what was its name?

6) Clive Brittain's tough and talented stayer got better with age and won successive Epsom Coronation Cups in 2003 and 2004, firstly with Philip Robinson and then with Darryll Holland. Who was he?

7) This very talented Guy Harwood-trained colt was unlucky with injuries but nevertheless, partnered by Pat Eddery, was a very successful Group horse. Unbeaten at two, he won the Sussex Stakes and the QEII, the latter by five lengths with a superb turn of foot in

1988. At four, he won the Queen Anne at Royal Ascot and *Timeform* rated him the top miler of his generation. Who was he?

8) I saw this Con Horgan trained horse win his prep race for the Ebor at Salisbury in 1985 but took no notice. More fool me! He won at York with Paul Cook up at 20-1. Who was he?

9) This gelding, who was nearly killed early on in a tussle with a lorry, ended up winning the 1986 Grand National when his connections were trainer Michael Oliver and jockey Richard Dunwoody. Who was he?

10) This horse might save a few lives! He was trained in Ireland by Charles Byrnes and won the 2009 Albert Bartlett Novices Hurdle at Cheltenham before coming back again in 2010 to take the RSA Chase, ridden on both occasions by Davy Russell. Who was he?

Quiz No. 24

ALPHABET ALLEY – X

All the answers in this category are horses beginning with 'X'

1) Put an X in front of a town in Hampshire and you produce the winner of the Portland at Doncaster and the July Cup at Newmarket in 1931. What was it called?

2) This horse was named after a Persian King and won Royal Ascot's Coventry Stakes in 1961, ridden by Doug Smith. It is the only one of these ten with two Xs in its name. Which is what?

3) Between 1858 and 1862 this horse finished third twice, fourth and fifth in the Grand National and its name means 'river god' in Greek if that helps any! What was it called?

4) Which Greek philosopher and soldier won Cheltenham's Coral Cup Hurdle in 2003, trained by Tony Martin and ridden by Mick Fitzgerald?

5) Now a USA radio station, it won the Stewards Cup at Goodwood and the Portland at Doncaster in 1905. Who was it?

6) Which Andre Fabre-trained horse won four of its five two-year-old races, including the Dewhurst at Newmarket, before also taking the Craven Stakes at the same course in the following season of 1998?

7) Some films fall into the category of the horse trained by Mark Johnston that won three races at Wolverhampton between 2016 and 2018. What was its name?

8) A busy sprinter for trainer Amanda Perrett between 1998 and 2005, with six of its nine wins coming at Hamilton for jockeys as diverse as Carl Lowther, Dean Mernagh, Diane Jones, Claire Stretton and Paul Hanagan, it was also a horse sung about by Dave Dee, Dozy, Beaky, Mick and Titch, and Olivia Newton-John. What was it called?

9) Which horse trained by Richard Hannon won a maiden over six furlongs at Goodwood with Richard Hughes in the saddle in 2001 and went on to run four more times without troubling the judges?

10) It's getting tough to complete the ten so I apologise for scraping the barrel with the horse and the clue. Which horse, at 33-1, fell in the last Grand National of the 19th century and is currently a medical records company in Denver, Colorado? Good luck with that!

Quiz No. 25

ALPHABET ALLEY – Y

All the answers in this category are horses beginning with 'Y'

1) The Great Metropolitan over two and a quarter miles at Epsom was a much more significant early season race in 1949 than it is today. Which chocolate biscuit and child's toy won it that year on a course that appropriately has its ups and downs?

2) Unfortunately, this doesn't come again! Freddie Head won the French Derby on it in 1976 for trainer Maurice Zilber. What was it called?

3) Only one horse beginning with Y has ever won the Derby and it came very early on in the second running of the race in 1781. His sire, and the clue is in his name, was arguably the greatest racehorse of all, never beaten, and, some say, never extended. Who won that 1781 Derby?

4) Now, from 1781, let's leap forward to our own time. Which Willie Mullins-trained horse won the Ballymore Novices' Hurdle at Cheltenham in 2016, and followed up in 2017 with the JLT Novices' Chase, with Ruby Walsh on board on both occasions?

5) Which cheese, trained by Jim Goldie, won 12 times on the turf over six or seven furlongs between 2003 and 2009 at Ayr, Doncaster, Hamilton, Haydock Park and Redcar?

6) Kieren Fallon and William Haggas won the Hunt Cup of 1996 with a horse that is an anagram of a horse that won four successive Ascot Gold Cups. Which horse won that Hunt Cup?

7) Wet and colourful, this horse, trained by Scobie Breasley and ridden by Tommy Carter, took Royal Ascot's Queen's Vase in 1970, before finishing second in both the Henry II Stakes and the Chester Cup the following season. Who was he?

8) As a two-year-old in 1971, he won both the Washington Singer Stakes at Newbury and the Royal Lodge at Ascot. However, his career failed to take off after that and trainer Noel Murless had to defend him

against critics calling him a 'talking horse'. He shared his name, except the first letter, with the first name of the Wimbledon champion of 1954. What was he called?

9) The winner of the Jockey Club Cup at Newmarket in 1954 shared his name with the person who had once inhabited the skull that Hamlet contemplated. What was his name?

10) Which horse, trained by Paddy Prendergast and ridden by Lester Piggott, won the Coventry Stakes at Royal Ascot and the Gimcrack at York in 1965 but failed to deliver as a three-year-old?

Quiz No. 26

ALPHABET ALLEY – Z

All the answers in this category are horses beginning with 'Z'

1) The winner of the 1959 Irish Grand National has a name that rhymes with a Japanese motorbike! What was it?

2) Perhaps it was written in the stars that which horse would win the 1924 Irish St Leger?

3) Which fictitious Greek won Royal Ascot's Queen's Vase in 1968 for trainer Paddy Prendergast and jockey Ron Hutchinson?

4) Which shallow Dutch bay won the 2011 November Handicap at Doncaster for John Gosden and Robert Havlin?

5) This horse, the winner of the 1976 Hennessy at Newbury, trained by Peter Bailey and ridden by Ian Watkinson, sadly lost his life in the following year's Grand National. Who was he?

6) Which two colts are the only ones beginning with a Z to win the 2,000 Guineas, doing so while trained in France in 1982 and 1993?

7) One of the most successful racehorses of the 1950s was trained initially in Ireland where in 1954 he took both the Irish Derby and St Leger. Coming to England with Cecil Boyd-Rochford, he won the Ascot Stakes and Goodwood Cup in 1956 before fracturing a cannon bone. Amazingly, he bounced back to land the Ascot Gold Cup in 1957. Who was he?

8) In 1953 Bill Payne and Lester Piggott combined to win Epsom's Coronation Cup. Almost half a century later a horse with the same name won the Lincoln at Doncaster ridden by Simon Whitworth and trained by David Arbuthnot. What name was involved each time?

9) After winning five times as a two-year-old, this Aidan O'Brien-trained colt produced his best performance as a racehorse in defeat when he became the only horse in Frankel's three-year-old season to come within a length of him in the 2011 St James Palace Stakes at Royal Ascot. Who was he?

10) In the history of Cheltenham's Triumph Hurdle, three horses beginning
with Z have won it. The first was trained by Fred Rimell in 1972, the
second by Nicky Henderson in 2009 and the third by Paul Nicholls in
2011. Who are the three horses?

Quiz No. 27

ANYTHING GOES

1) Who was the only jockey to ride more than one Grand National winner in the 1990s?

2) What is the link between Red Pixie, Red Sweeney and Red Candle, besides the obvious?

3) Who are the only two trainers to win the Grand National in this century and the last one?

4) Who is the only jockey to win the Arkle Chase three times in a row at Cheltenham, doing so in 1992, 1993 and 1994?

5) John Lowe rode the last-ever winner at Lanark racecourse on 18 October 1977 with a horse that featured the names of two satirists and comedians who had their own television show. What was the horse called?

6) Since 2009 three horses with 'Harry' in their name have been in the frame in Ascot's Long Walk Hurdle. What were their names?

7) What did owner William Brophy do in 1880 that is unique in Irish racing with two horses, one called King of the Bees and the other Controller?

8) Knock the last word off the winner of the 2000 edition of the Oaks at Epsom and you produce the winner of the race 20 years later. Who are the two fillies?

9) The Mares' Hurdle at Cheltenham has been dominated by Willie Mullins, but the first one in 2008 and the most recent in 2021 have both been won by English-trained horses from Donald McCain and Denise Foster. They also have contrasting colours in their names. Who are they?

10) Besides Frankie Dettori, who has done so twice, who is the only jockey to win back-to-back Arcs this century?

Quiz No. 28

CHASING DREAMS AT THE CHELTENHAM FESTIVAL

1) Martin Pipe trained back-to-back winners of the Arkle Chase in 1997 and 1998, and again in 2004 and 2005. Since then, up to 2021, which three trainers have also won it in successive years?

2) The Ultima Handicap Chase was won three times in six years between 2009 and 2014 by trainer Jonjo O'Neill with assistance in the saddle from AP McCoy on the first occasion and Richie McLernon in the last two. Which three horses was he successful with?

3) The RSA Novices' Chase has sometimes pointed up a future Gold Cup winner. Which three winners of the race in this century have gone on to claim the big one after winning it?

4) The Glenfarcas Cross Country Chase was established in 2005 and Tiger Roll has recently been successful in it on three occasions. Previously, only two horses had won it twice, one trained by Enda Bolger and the other by Philip Hobbs. Who were they?

5) Since its establishment in 2011 the JLT Novices' Chase has been won by just one horse with a colour in its name. Willie Mullins trained it for the 2016 edition of the race. What was its name?

6) Another Willie Mullins-trained horse had the shortest name of a Ryanair Chase winner since it was inaugurated in 2005 when it was successful in 2020. What was it called?

7) Since Fulke Walwyn's name was added to the Kim Muir Handicap Chase in 1991, only one horse with a city in its name has won the race and did so in 2020. What was the Gordon Elliott-trained horse called?

8) Between 2009 and 2014 the winner of the Foxhunter Chase was trained by a bird, a Champions League-winning manager, a cops-and-robbers TV show and a Beatle. Who were the four winning trainers?

9) The Centenary Novices' Handicap Chase, between 2005 and 2021, has been hard for a trainer to capture more than once. Only one has achieved the feat. Who?

A) Philip Hobbs B) Ferdy Murphy C) Paul Nicholls
D) Venetia Williams

10) The curtain comes down each year with the Johnny Henderson Grand Annual. Who was the last horse to win it and then go on to win the Queen Mother Champion Chase two years later?

Quiz No. 29

CLASSIC CONUNDRUMS

Ten multiple-choice questions on the English classics.

1) The great opera composer Giuseppe Verdi died in 1901, the same year that which of his operas won the 1,000 Guineas at Newmarket?

   A) Aida B) La Traviata C) Masked Ball D) Rigoletto

2) Who is the only post-war trainer to win the 1,000 Guineas in four different decades?

   A) Henry Cecil B) Noel Murless C) Vincent O'Brien
   D) Michael Stoute

3) Between the end of the Second World War and the close of the century, which one of these jockeys failed to win back-to-back 2,000 Guineas?

   A) Gianfranco Dettori B) Pat Eddery C) Mick Kinane
   D) Lester Piggott

4) At 66-1, which horse won the 2,000 Guineas at the biggest price since World War Two?

   A) Gilles De Retz (1956) B) Mon Fils (1973)
   C) Night of Thunder (2014) D) Rockavon (1961)

5) Aidan O'Brien and John Gosden, up to 2021, have trained nine of the last ten winners of the Oaks. Who was the only trainer outside those two to win the race since their run started in 2012?

   A) Ralph Beckett B) Michael Bell C) Ed Dunlop D) William Haggas

6) Which golf course won the 1821 Oaks?

   A) Augusta B) Carnoustie C) Troon D) Wentworth

7) Which member of England's 1966 World Cup-winning team rode the 1857 Derby winner?

   A) Alan Ball B) Jack Charlton C) Bobby Moore D) Ray Wilson

8) Up to 2021, these four jockeys have all won the Derby on short-priced horses. Which one of them was on the shortest-priced winner?

   A) Frankie Dettori B) Joseph O'Brien C) Lester Piggott
   D) Walter Swinburn

9) Which trainer won the St Leger twice in the 1960s, twice in the 1970s and twice in the 1980s?

   A) Vincent O'Brien B) Henry Cecil C) Dick Hern
   D) Fulke Johnson-Houghton

10) Up to 2021, four jockeys have won back-to-back St Legers this century, but only one of them has won it with both his horses at the same price of 3-1. Who is he?

   A) William Buick B) Frankie Dettori C) Ryan Moore
   D) Andrea Atzeni

Quiz No. 30

CRYPTIC CLASSIC-WINNING JOCKEYS

Can you name these Classic-winning jockeys? You are given the race they won and the year plus a cryptic clue.

1) 1996 Derby – Bookmakers

2) 1982 2,000 Guineas – Part of the body

3) 1980 1,000 Guineas – Wake someone up

4) 1962 Derby – What a forester might do

5) 1972 1,000 Guineas – Conceal from sight

6) 2004 St Leger – Blackburn Rovers striker who was joint-top goalscorer with Jimmy Greaves in 1963/64

7) 2012 Oaks – Sounds like a cross between a cow and an aged relative!

8) 2007 St Leger – It's supposed to favour the brave

9) 1978 Oaks – One of the Fab Four

10) 1969 2,000 Guineas – Morse's sidekick

Quiz No. 31

CRYPTIC GRAND NATIONAL-WINNING JOCKEYS – PART 1

Can you name these jockeys who had winning rides in the big race? You are given the year and a cryptic clue.

1) 2001 – Found in a hotel

2) 1987 – Chess piece

3) 1906 – South-coast resort

4) 1947 – Earlier heavyweight champion of the world

5) 1989 – Found on cold mornings

6) 1966 – Appropriately enough given the year, a member of the winners of a battle 900 years before

7) 2013 – Medical condition

8) 1981 – Fictional wonder horse

9) 1975 – Ipswich Town right-back when they won the league in 1961/62

10) 1976 – 'Peerage' author

Quiz No. 32

CRYPTIC GRAND NATIONAL-WINNING JOCKEYS – PART 2

1) 1980 – Wins the Grand National one year, then follows it up by scoring in the FA Cup final two years later!

2) 1935 – there used to be 36 of these in the Grand National, but two have fallen by the wayside recently

3) 1956 – Private detective

4) 1967 – County town

5) 1979 – Area of south-west London

6) 1971 – Occupation

7) 2004 – American Civil War genius now denigrated by those whose idea of history doesn't extend beyond a fight between 'goodies' and 'baddies'

8) 1957 and 1962 – Season

9) 1939 – Area of Greater Manchester associated with villainous doctor

10) 1865 – Midlands city

Quiz No. 33

THE DEFINITE ARTICLE

All these answers begin with 'The'

1) This colt showed real bravery to get past Hot Grove to win the 1977 Derby for his connections, who were Lester Piggott, Vincent O'Brien and Robert Sangster. Who was he?

2) This horse shares his name with a Dire Straits song and, piloted by Charlie Smirke, he was the top sprinter of 1946, landing the Wokingham, the July Cup and the Nunthorpe. Who was he?

3) Leaving nothing to chance, Lester Piggott and Henry Cecil teamed up at Nottingham on 27 April 1982 to gain the owner of this horse the princely sum of £897. It shared its name with a popular novel by Luke Reinhardt. What was it called?

4) He may have been deposed by the Iranian revolution of 1979, but 33 years earlier he was successful in the Portland at Doncaster. Who was he?

5) Which county town obliged at 20-1 in the 1976 Lincoln at Doncaster for trainer Brian Swift and jockey Geoff Lewis?

6) Sergio Garcia, Pablo Picasso and Rafael Nadal spring to mind when considering the 1970 Scottish Grand National winner, trained by Ken Oliver and ridden by Barry Brogan. What was its name?

7) If something goes wrong with your drains, this is the bloke that helps the bloke who's come to fix it! It also won the 1955 running of the Wokingham at Royal Ascot, partnered by Duncan Keith and trained by Herbert Smyth. What was it called?

8) The strip of water that joins southern England to the Isle of Wight took the 1979 Goodwood Stakes for Henry Cecil and Lester Piggott. What was its name?

9) Which Fulke Walwyn-trained horse had a healthy bite at three large plums of the jumps game when he won the 1971 King George, the 1973 Gold Cup and the 1974 Whitbread?

10) Environmentalists might show some concern about the 2016 winner of Newmarket's Middle Park Stakes trained by Mark Johnston and ridden by Joe Fanning, but I expect a few wildebeest breathed a sigh of relief! Which horse won the race?

Quiz No. 34

THE DERBY

1) Which four horses, beginning with an A, have won the Derby this century?

2) Which famous opera singer won the emotional Derby of 1953?

3) Which current Liverpool footballer shares his first name with a post-war winner of the Derby?

4) Pan and Sam in the early years of the 19th century are the only two three-letter winners of the Derby, and only two four-letter winners of the race have occurred since Orby in 1907. They won in 1979 and 1999. Who are they?

5) Which two dogs won the Derby in 1826 and 1831?

   A) Lapdog and Spaniel B) Jack Russell and Boxer C) Bloodhound and Alsatian D) Bulldog and Retriever

6) Which Wagner opera won the 1849 running of the Derby?

   A) Tannhauser B) The Flying Dutchman C) Lohengrin D) Parsifal

7) The Derby winner of 1800 shares its name with the surname of a Grand National-winning jockey from over 180 years later. What was the Derby winner's name?

8) Beethoven's wonderful 'Piano Trio, Opus 97' won the 1799 Derby 12 years before he wrote it! What was the winner called?

9) Strangely enough, the 1894 Derby was won by Soviet-built cars 79 years before they were manufactured. Who won that Derby?

10) Which two West Ham United players from this century won the Derby in 1786 and 1822?

Quiz No. 35

FAVOURITE RACEHORSES ON THE FLAT
No. 1 BRIGADIER GERARD

1) Between Tudor Minstrel in the late 1940s and Frankel in the current century, Brigadier Gerard was almost certainly the greatest miler on the English turf. He had one owner, one trainer and one jockey throughout his racing career. Who were that trio?

2) How are Sparkler and Gold Rod unique to Brigadier Gerard's career?

3) Brigadier Gerard won 17 of his 18 races, and everyone knows that Roberto was the only horse to lower his colours in the 1972 Benson & Hedges Gold Cup at York, despite the Brigadier putting up the best time fractions of his career. Which Arc winner finished fourth in that race?

4) Brigadier Gerard won on his debut at 100-7 on 24 June 1970 over five furlongs when he beat Lester Piggott's mount Young and Foolish, who finished fourth of five. Those who took the 8-15 offered about his chance, whether young or old, certainly were foolish! Where did Brigadier Gerard win first time out?

5) The place money for coming second at York in 1972 was greater than the purses he won in ten of his 17 wins. True or false?

6) Which French horse, trained by Alec Head and ridden by his son Freddie, was third behind Brigadier Gerard in the 1972 King George at Ascot, and second to him in the Champion Stakes that year in the Brigadier's last race, before going on to sire successive Arc winners in Detroit and Gold River?

7) Brigadier Gerard raced with distinction at seven tracks. Which one is missing from the list? – Ascot, Goodwood, Newbury, Newmarket, Sandown Park, York.

8) Which race at Newmarket did Brigadier Gerard win to close out his two-year-old career in October 1970?

9) He started at odds-on in 15 of his 18 races, and outside his debut, the biggest price he went off at was in his greatest moment, namely the defeat of Mill Reef in the 1971 2,000 Guineas at Newmarket. What price was he returned at?

10) Among his successes were the St James's Palace Stakes, the Sussex Stakes, the Lockinge, the Prince of Wales Stakes, the Eclipse, the King George and two QEII Stakes. But which two races that begin with the same five letters did he also win?

Quiz No. 36

FAVOURITE RACEHORSES ON THE FLAT
No. 2 DANCING BRAVE

1) Dancing Brave won eight of his ten races over a two-year career, making his winning debut as a two-year-old in the Dorking Stakes at which course?

2) After victory in the Soham House Stakes at Newmarket he was put away until the spring when he won his first race up as a three-year-old, becoming favourite for the 2,000 Guineas in the process. Which race did he win?

3) He was enormously impressive in the Guineas, beating which highly touted horse of Maktoum Al Maktoum's, trained by Michael Stoute, who had considerable success later in his career back to six furlongs?

4) The 1986 Derby was the most talked-about for many years and everyone knows the circumstances that contrived to get Dancing Brave beaten by Shahrastani on the day. Who owned, trained and rode the rather fortunate winner?

5) Dancing Brave experienced two jockeys in his racing days: Greville Starkey and Pat Eddery. Did they each ride him five times, or did one ride him more than the other, and if so, which?

6) After a superb performance in the Eclipse, Dancing Brave and Shahrastani met again in the King George at Ascot in an eagerly awaited contest. It was assumed that they would finish one and two again, and Dancing Brave duly got his revenge. But it wasn't his Epsom rival that came second but another horse from the Stoute stable. Who was it, and for a bonus point, which winner of the race the previous year could only finish fifth this time?

7) We have seen that Dancing Brave won at Ascot, Newmarket and Sandown Park, but which other English racecourse did he win on?

8) Dancing Brave had his greatest moment in the 1986 Arc at Longchamp when he beat the best Arc field since Sea Bird II's famous victory in 1965 with an exhilarating turn of foot inside the final furlong. Which colt who had won the French Derby had looked the winner but had to be content with second place?

9) The only other horse to beat him besides Shahrastani was Manila in Dancing Brave's final race. What was that race, and where was it held?

10) Although he was no Northern Dancer, as a sire Dancing Brave did produce a Derby winner in the 1990s at Epsom. Who was it?

Quiz No. 37

FAVOURITE RACEHORSES ON THE FLAT
No. 3 FRANKEL

1) If I lived another 100 years I would not expect to see anything this good again. It wasn't just the 14 wins in 14 starts, it was the awesome dominance in the way he won. The horse that got closest to him did so in his debut race at Newmarket as a two-year-old in August 2010, running Frankel to half a length. Trained by John Gosden, he went on to win the King George. Who was he?

2) The declared going for that first race was repeated in his final race, but not in any of the 12 in between. What was it?

3) That first race was also the only time that Frankel went off odds-against in a race. What price was he that day and what was the shortest price he went off at in his career, which came in the 2012 running of the Sussex Stakes at Goodwood?

4) Frankel only raced in England. Besides Goodwood and Newmarket, which I've already mentioned, which four other courses did he compete on, and which one of the four did he face just two opponents on?

5) The only horse to finish second to Frankel three times already figures in another category in this book, but which Godolphin horse was second to Frankel in the 2012 Sussex Stakes and in the International at York in the same year, its name suggesting the distance between the two horses?

6) Frankel experienced a scare in the last race of his career at Ascot when he lost four lengths at the start in the 2012 Champion Stakes. However, he was able to sail past a French horse trained by Corine Barande-Barbe to a tremendous heartfelt ovation. Which horse came second?

7) Which race did Frankel win in 2011 and 2012, thus becoming the only horse to do so since its inception in 1878?

8) When Frankel won the Juddmonte International at York in 2012 it was his eighth successive Group One win and thus broke the record of which horse who had won seven in a row earlier in the century?

9) Although his dominance in the 2012 Queen Anne at Ascot could barely be believed, perhaps the most thrilling moment of his or any other horse's career came at the half-way mark of the 2011 2,000 Guineas when he completely destroyed that classic field and took 15 lengths out of them in a few strides! As he slowed down with the job done which horse trained by Richard Hannon Senior and ridden by Richard Hughes, followed him home six lengths behind?

10) Frankel probably kept Henry Cecil going through the pain of his last years and his patience and skill in placing him were vital. Which of his progeny has equalled Frankel's record of winning on successive Champions' Days at Ascot?

Quiz No. 38

FAVOURITE RACEHORSES ON THE FLAT
No. 4 GIANT'S CAUSEWAY

1) He was certainly a giant, but what other name was he given by racing journalists due to his phenomenal toughness on the racecourse?

2) He went into battle 13 times in his career over two years, winning nine and coming second in the other four. As a two-year-old he took Ireland's Futurity Stakes, winning from his stable companion who had a sideline in musical composition. Who did he beat?

   A) Bach B) Beethoven C) Brahms D) Bruckner

3) He opened his three-year-old career by beating Tarry Flynn over seven furlongs at the Curragh in early April in which race?

4) In his 2000 season he became the first horse to win how many Group Ones as a three-year-old?

5) Which horse trained by Michael Stoute and ridden by Kieren Fallon beat Giant's Causeway in that year's 2,000 Guineas?

6) Why racegoers loved him was because, a bit like Persian Punch, he seemed to idle in front and wait to be eyeballed by a rival before holding up a 'They shalt not pass' sign and sticking his neck out all the way to the line. The winning margin was a neck or less in five of his races, but he frustrated the connections of one horse by a head in both the Eclipse and the Juddmonte International after looking beaten both times. Who was the narrowly beaten horse?

7) Mick Kinane was on board Giant's Causeway in 12 of his 13 outings. Who was the only other jockey to ride him and in which race?

8) He ran at ten venues. Which one, where he made his debut over six furlongs in a two-year-old maiden on 21 July 1999, is missing from the list? – Ascot, Churchill Downs, The Curragh, Goodwood, Leopardstown, Longchamp, Newmarket, Sandown and York.

9) Michael Stoute was one of the biggest sufferers from the sheer will to win of Giant's Causeway and another of his horses finished third to him in the St James's Palace Stakes and the Sussex Stakes in 2000. Who was he?

10) After defeat in the QEII at Ascot, he went for his final race in America to contest the Breeders' Cup Classic. He ran a blinder, but, unfortunately, Mick Kinane chose the wrong moment to get the whip stuck in his reins and the race was lost by a neck. The rather fortunate winning horse went on to be the only horse to win the race twice when successful again in 2001. Who was he?

Quiz No. 39

FAVOURITE RACEHORSES ON THE FLAT
No. 5 PERSIAN PUNCH

1) Persian Punch was much loved by racing aficionados for time and again sticking his neck out when all seemed lost, plucking victory by a whisker from the jaws of defeat. The biggest price he won at was 20-1 on his racecourse debut on 13 May 1996 ridden by Tony Procter in a three-year-olds Class E maiden over a mile and a quarter on which course?

   A) Newbury B) Salisbury C) Windsor D) Yarmouth

2) Persian Punch ran on four courses outside England. They were The Curragh, Deauville, Flemington and Longchamp. He won on one of them on 20 August 2000. Which one?

3) In England, he won more than once on six courses. They were Doncaster, Goodwood, Newmarket, Salisbury, Sandown and York. Which of these did he win on the most?

4) He won 20 races in his career, but none of them came at Ascot. True or false?

5) Kieren Fallon, Tony Procter, Philip Robinson and Walter Swinburn all won races with Persian Punch, but who were the only four jockeys that did so more than once?

6) Which Group Three race at Newmarket did he win in 2000, 2002 and 2003?

7) He was on the mark three times in the same event at Sandown Park as well, taking the prize in 1997, 1998 and 2000. The sponsor was Bonusprint, but what was the event's traditional name?

8) He recorded doubles at Goodwood in 2001 and 2003, and at York in 1998 and 2001 in which two races?

9) Which Ascot Gold Cup winner finished second to Persian Punch at Sandown Park in 1997 and at York in 1998?

10) The stand-outs in his photo-finish wins were two at York and Goodwood, when he got back up to beat an Alan Jarvis-trained horse, and, arguably his most exciting and greatest moment, when he beat a John Dunlop-trained classic winner in his last win in October 2003 after a titanic tussle between the pair at Newmarket. Who were his two worthy opponents?

Quiz No. 40

FAVOURITE RACEHORSES OVER THE JUMPS
No. 1 ARKLE

1) Those five letters put us in rarefied air. The authorities produced one set of weights if he was declared to run and another if he wasn't. Compliments don't come much greater. Who were his trainer and owner, and what did the latter name him after?

2) Such was his fame that before the media madness we now live in thousands sent him gifts, letters and cards, some addressed simply 'Arkle, Ireland'. What name was he known by in Ireland?

3) Pat Taaffe rode him in 28 of his 35 starts. The other four riders to do so were TP Burns, Mark Hely-Hutchinson, Liam McLoughlin and Paddy Woods. Which one of those four didn't win on him?

4) Which was the only course he won on over the jumps and on the flat?

5) In England he appeared on just five courses. What were they, and which two did he remain undefeated on?

6) Although to some extent his fame comes from his three Cheltenham Gold Cups of 1964, 1965 and 1966, and in doing so producing the intensive English v Irish competition annually at the event, like Crisp, he's also remembered for defying or just failing to defy heavy burdens in top handicaps. On 26 November 1966 in the Hennessy he was beaten into second place by Stalbridge Colonist, but was giving him what number of pounds in weight?

7) Besides the Cheltenham Gold Cup, which other race did Arkle win in the three successive years of 1964, 1965 and 1966?

8) The rivalry with Mill House was a key theme in Arkle's story, but which horse beat them both, the former in the 1964 Whitbread, and the latter in the 1966 King George VI Chase, Arkle's last race?

9) Which was the only Irish course that Arkle ran on four times undefeated?

10) Not many owners wanted to take Arkle on in his Cheltenham Gold Cup triumphs. Only nine horses did so. They were Mill House twice, King's Nephew, Stoney Crossing, Caduval, Sartorius, Snaigow, Hunch, Dormant and one other horse who had been a previous Cheltenham Gold Cup winner. Who was it?

Quiz No. 41

FAVOURITE RACEHORSES OVER THE JUMPS
No. 2 DENMAN

1) Denman, trained by Paul Nicholls, was probably the best galloper with a high cruising speed we have been privileged to see in action and his powerful front running was such that in his pomp few could live with him. In the circumstances it wasn't hard to see that he was given what nickname?

2) As well as winning the 2008 Cheltenham Gold Cup with an awesome display, he finished second in the race no fewer than three times. To which three horses?

3) After winning a point-to-point at Liscarroll with Colman Sweeney in March 2005, he experienced four more jockeys in his career. Who were they, and which one of them had a 100 per cent record on him while which one never won on him?

4) He appeared on six English courses, two Irish and one Welsh. What were the three non-English ones he ran on?

5) Which two English courses did he have a 100 per cent record on?

6) In the nearly three and a half years between October 2005 and February 2009 only one horse beat Denman. It was trained by Noel Meade and Denman finished second to it in the RSA Novices' Hurdle at Cheltenham on 15 March 2006. Who was the horse?

7) For me it was those two weight-defying wins in the Hennessy at Newbury in 2007 and 2009 that made him so special. There's still only one horse who has also won two Hennessys. Who is it?

8) It was only fitting that Newbury, therefore, was the course that honoured him with his own race. What had it previously been known as?

9) The only Grand National winner to finish second to Denman did so on 11 November 2006 in a novices chase at Cheltenham. Who was he?

10) It was a shame that his superb career ended with six defeats, but what was incredible was that his second Hennessy came over a year after an announcement from the stable of what condition on 23 September 2008?

Quiz No. 42

FAVOURITE RACEHORSES OVER THE JUMPS
No. 3 DESERT ORCHID

1) There have been few more thrilling jumpers over the years than this instantly recognisable grey-bordering-on-white trained by David Elsworth for owner Richard Burridge. Dessie was a risk taker and the crowds that flocked to see him loved him for it. The first and last of his 70 races were on the same course and ended the same way. Where did he run and what happened?

2) He won 34 races. Which jockey was on board for half of those wins?

3) All his races bar one were in England. He won the only one that wasn't at even money in 1990. What was the event and where was it held?

4) In England he raced more than once at seven courses. They were Aintree, Ascot, Cheltenham, Exeter, Kempton, Sandown and Wincanton. His penultimate race took place at a new course for him. Which one?

5) Despite hating going left-handed, he won a slow-motion finish in heavy going to take the Cheltenham Gold Cup in 1989, and finished third in that event the following two seasons to which two horses?

6) Desert Orchid's greatest claim to fame was his four wins in Kempton's King George VI Chase. Of the eight horses that finished in the frame behind him in those races, which was the only one to go on to win the event?

7) There are not one but two races named in his honour. One of them is obviously at Kempton, but where is the other one held?

8) Which horse trained by Sue Smith did Desert Orchid meet three times between February and April 1988, coming second to him at Wincanton before beating him twice at Aintree and Sandown, and again in that year's King George?

9) Desert Orchid won for the first time on a left-handed track when he landed Aintree's Martell Cup in 1988. In the following season the horse he had beaten in the Cheltenham Gold Cup turned the tables on him the following month by winning the Aintree race when Dessie fell. Who won the race?

10) Desert Orchid's last win came in February 1991 in the Agfa Diamond Chase at Sandown, while the previous February had seen him lump 12st 3lbs around Kempton Park to take the Racing Post Trophy. Which English composer did he beat into second place that day?

A) Delius B) Elgar C) Purcell D) Walton

Quiz No. 43

FAVOURITE RACEHORSES OVER THE JUMPS
No. 4 KAUTO STAR

1) Who was the only horse to beat Kauto Star four times?

2) Who became the only jockey to have a 100 per cent win record accompanying Kauto Star when they took the 2005 Tingle Creek at Sandown together in his only ride on the horse?

3) Who is the only jockey to ride Kauto Star in a race in England and not win on him?

4) Which course did Kauto Star appear on the most times?

   A) Auteuil B) Cheltenham C) Haydock D) Kempton

5) Which horse finished in the frame behind Kauto Star in the 2006 and 2007 King George, the 2007 and 2009 Cheltenham Gold Cup and the 2007 Betfair Chase, finishing second three times and third twice?

6) The long and the short of it! By how many lengths did Kauto Star beat Madison Du Berlais in the 2009 King George, and which horse did Kauto Star beat by a nose after a thrilling encounter in the same year's Betfair Chase at Haydock, with the third horse 24 lengths away?

7) In the 2008 Cheltenham Gold Cup Kauto Star finished second, sandwiched between two of his stablemates, thus making it a 1-2-3 for trainer Paul Nicholls. Who were the other two horses?

8) Which horse did Kauto Star finish third behind in the 2010 King George and the 2011 Cheltenham Gold Cup, but beat in the 2011 Betfair Chase and the 2011 King George?

9) Kauto Star is the only horse to win two different Grade One events four times, and the only horse to win a Grade One race in seven consecutive seasons. True or false?

10) Why did Kauto Star land a million-pound bonus in the 2006/07 season? (I expect he took all the horses in the Nicholls' yard out for a slap-up meal and still had change to brighten up his stall with a lick of paint.)

Quiz No. 44

FAVOURITE RACEHORSES OVER THE JUMPS
No. 5 MOSCOW FLYER

1) Moscow Flyer made more than the odd jumping error in his races, but if he didn't you could count on him winning. In April 2001 he finished behind Colonel Yeagar at Gowran Park and in the same month four years later he finished behind Rathgar Beau at Punchestown. Between those two, he never finished behind another horse, he either won or fell or unseated in every race for four years! How many races was it?

2) Who trained Moscow Flyer?

3) He was successful in 26 of his 44 races, 25 times with Barry Geraghty up top and once, at Punchestown in the Irish Champion Novices' Hurdle in 2000, with which jockey?

4) Moscow Flyer ran 21 times in Ireland before he came over to England to run at Cheltenham in 2002. Which race did he win that year at the festival?

5) Which Derby winner was Moscow Flyer's grandsire?

    A) The Minstrel B) Nijinsky C) Roberto D) Sir Ivor

6) In his racing career in England Moscow Flyer competed on just three courses. On which one of the three did he maintain a 100 per cent record?

7) Which of the following Irish courses was the only one he had a 100 per cent record on?

    A) Down Royal B) Fairyhouse C) Gowran Park D) Navan

8) Which legendary Irish horse did Moscow Flyer defeat twice in his hurdling days?

9) Among the highlights of his great career were doubles between 2003 and 2005 in three races that don't come much bigger. They were (a) The Queen Mother Champion Chase (b) The Tingle Creek, and (c) The Melling Chase. Can you produce the two winning years in each case?

10) A tough one to finish. Moscow Flyer appeared on ten racecourses in his career. Which was the only one he didn't win on?

Quiz No. 45

THE GEOGRAPHY OF THE DERBY

1) The Derby-winning horses in 1969 and 1973 are both to be found in north Norfolk. Who were they?

2) Which area in west London won the Derby in 1851?

   A) Richmond B) St Margarets C) Teddington D) Twickenham

3) Which Derby winner of the current century can be found in Hyde Park?

4) The 1844 Derby winner was the birthplace of golfer Tiger Woods. What was its name?

5) Which capital city won the 1806 Derby?

   A) London B) Lisbon C) Madrid D) Paris

6) Which Yorkshire racecourse won the Derby in 1873?

   A) Beverley B) Doncaster C) Pontefract D) Wetherby

7) Which area of London won the 1839 Derby?

   A) Bloomsbury B) Edgware C) Highbury D) Hampstead

8) Which Scottish location won the 1888 running of the Derby?

   A) The Clyde B) Loch Lomond C) Ayrshire D) Midlothian

9) The winner of the 1854 Derby was the place in Hampshire The Troggs came from. What horse won it?

10) The 1934 Derby winner who was ridden by Charlie Smirke had a name that referenced a town in the south of England. The horse went on to win the St Leger later that season. What was it called?

Quiz No. 46

GREYS

1) There's something about a grey horse that gets your attention as you watch a race and they now have an annual race of their own. Where is it held?

2) Which grey was victorious in the 2007 running of the Supreme Novices' Hurdle at Cheltenham for jockey Davy Condon and trainer Willie Mullins?

3) Which grey colt was touched off at Epsom in the 1997 Derby but gained compensation by landing the St Leger, trained by John Dunlop and ridden by Pat Eddery?

4) Jockey Bobby Beasley and trainer Fred Rimell combined to produce the first Grand National-winning grey for 90 years when they took the Aintree race in 1961 with which horse?

5) All those years before, in 1871, which animal had been the first grey to win the Grand National?

A) The Bear B) The Fox C) The Lamb D) The Panther

6) Which grey horse gave Richard Johnson his sole win in the Champion Hurdle at Cheltenham in 2003?

7) The 2012 Grand National at Aintree produced a third winning grey horse over 50 years after the last one when who won the race by the shortest-ever margin, trained by Paul Nicholls and ridden by Daryl Jacob?

8) The public loved the front-running enthusiastic jumper that, trained by Howard Johnson and ridden by Graham Lee, won the 2004 Scottish Grand National in great style under a weight that hadn't been carried in the previous 30 years. Who was he?

9) Another horse adored by the racing public was this bold jumper trained by Nicky Richards who won 17 times in his career, most notably claiming three Old Roan Chases at Aintree in 2007, 2009 and 2010. Who was he?

10) Let's finish with yet another grey with a large fan club. Uniquely, he is the only horse to win Kempton's King George VI Chase twice in the same calendar year of 1996, one at Sandown held over to the January from the previous year and the other at Kempton on the normal Boxing Day of 1996. Who was he?

Quiz No. 47

GROUP ONES – No. 1
THE ASCOT GOLD CUP
VENUE – Ascot / DISTANCE - 2 and a half miles / FIRST RUN – 1807

1) In its second running in 1808 it was won by a horse with a racecourse for a name. What was it called?

   A) Brighton B) Goodwood C) Lingfield D) Sandown

2) The most successful horse in the race was the Aidan O'Brien-trained Yeats who completed a four-timer in the event in 2009. It was accompanied by three different jockeys. Who were they?

3) Henry Cecil had a brilliant Royal Ascot in 1987 and when heavy rain had changed the going for the Gold Cup jockey Steve Cauthen switched his intended mount for a mud lover who duly obliged by a large margin. Appropriately, its name means a song of triumph. What was it called?

4) Three of these horses were Gold Cup winners in 1882, 1927 and 1933 but the fourth is my own invention. Can you spot the impostor?

   A) Foxfire B) Foxhall C) Foxhunter D) Foxlaw

5) French trainer Elie Lellouche and jockey Olivier Peslier teamed up to win the 2005 renewal of the race which was run for the only time at York. With which horse?

6) Among many dual winners of the race were Fighting Charlie in 1965 and 1966, Le Moss in 1979 and 1980, Gildoran in 1984 and 1985 and Sadeem in 1988 and 1989. What did they all have in common?

7) Which Saeed bin Suroor-trained horse was the only one to win the race in the 20th and 21st centuries when it took the prize in 1998 and 2000?

8) Besides Aidan O'Brien's exploits with Yeats, which other trainer has won the race four times in a row between the end of the war and the end of the century?

   A) Francois Boutin B) Henry Cecil C) Guy Harwood
   D) Lord Huntingdon

9) In 1865 the race was won by a town in Cambridgeshire. Then, 33 years later, it was won by a supernatural being in human form with a tendency to trickery. The two horses have just one letter's difference in their short names. What were they called?

10) Which horse won the Ascot Gold Cup in 1981 and 1982 before going back in trip for the 1982 Arc and finding just one horse blocking what would have been a magnificent feat?

Quiz No. 48

GROUP ONES – No. 2
THE CHAMPION STAKES
VENUE – Newmarket and Ascot / DISTANCE – 1m 2f / FIRST RUN – 1877

1) Weaponry was heavily involved when the race was run at Newmarket for the first time in 1877. The winning jockey's name was Cannon and the winning horse's name was a rifle. But which one?

2) In 1997 two Michaels, Kinane and Stoute, combined to land the Champion Stakes with which horse?

3) Tristan has been the only winner of the race in three successive years, doing so in 1882, 1883 and 1884. Why might critics carp at his achievement?

4) Lester Piggott had the first of his five wins in the race in 1959 on a brilliant filly trained by Noel Murless. What was her name?

5) The last two wins of the 20th century in 1998 and 1999 were claimed by Alborada. Who were the successful jockey and trainer?

6) Ernest Fellows and fellow Australian jockey Bill Pyers must have hatched an extremely cunning plan when they landed the Champion Stakes in 1964 with which horse?

7) Which horse, trained by Henry Cecil and ridden by Tom Queally, completed an appropriate double in the race in its last running at Newmarket in 2010?

8) In its first year at Ascot in 2011 it became for just that once the richest British race in the calendar, but the prize went to France through the efforts of which horse?

9) That 2011 winner was trained by a woman, and another also did the trick with Noble Mission in 2014. Who were the two trainers?

10) 13 horses won the race more than once up to 2021, but who was the winning jockey when Triptych performed the feat in successive years in 1986 and 1987?

Quiz No. 49

GROUP ONES – No. 3
THE ECLIPSE
VENUE – Sandown Park / DISTANCE – 1m 2f / FIRST RUN – 1886

1) The race is named for Eclipse who proved to be no fool after being foaled on 1 April 1764. Many believe him to be the greatest of all and he retired undefeated after how many races?

   A) 15 B) 16 C) 17 D) 18

2) Since the war up to 2021, five horses have won the Eclipse and the Derby in the same season. Tulyar, Mill Reef and Nashwan did so in the 20th century, but which two have done so in the current century?

3) Perhaps the most exciting contest came in 2000 when Giant's Causeway just held on in typical fashion. The successful jockey, George Duffield, had won the race nine years earlier for trainer James Fanshawe on which horse?

4) There were a lot of unique elements to Scottish Rifle's win in the race in 1973. It was jockey Ron Hutchinson's only win in the race, and the same went for trainer John Dunlop and owner Sandy Struthers. What else was unique about it?

5) Up to 2021 who is the only trainer to win the Eclipse in successive seasons this century?

   A) John Gosden B) Aidan O'Brien C) Saeed bin Suroor
   D) Michael Stoute

6) Which Ray Charles song won the Eclipse in 1967 trained by Noel Murless and ridden by Bill Rickaby?

   A) Born to Lose B) Busted C) Crying Time D) Hit the road Jack

7) The winners of the Eclipse in 2002 and 2016 both started with the same four letters. Who were the two horses?

8) Which jockey won the last Eclipse of the 20th century on Compton Admiral and then took the race again four years later with Falbrav?

9) A horse trained by George Lambton and ridden by Tommy Weston won the Eclipse in 1931. Fifty-two years later the name returned again to win the Benson & Hedges Gold Cup at York for owner Robert Sangster, trainer Vincent O'Brien and jockey Pat Eddery. What was this name that seemed to bring out the best in more than one animal?

10) This last question is divided into four parts and could be called 'Literary Corner.'

   a) Which Sir Arthur Conan Doyle character won the race in 1972?

   b) Which 19th-century novelist appears in the name of the winning horse in 1979?

   c) Which novelist, whose life spanned the 19th and 20th centuries, is one half of the 1984 winner?

   d) Which novel with a massive reputation that many people will say they've read when they haven't won the 2017 renewal?

Quiz No. 50

GROUP ONES – No. 4
THE HAYDOCK SPRINT CUP
VENUE – Haydock Park / DISTANCE – 6f / FIRST RUN – 1966

1) Pools company Vernons were the first sponsors and the first winner did something that hasn't happened again when he followed up in 1967. Trained by Cyril Mitchell, the horse was owned by a well-known racing personality. What was the horse called and who owned him?

2) Why was the 1968 race not run?

   A) Fog B) Foot-and-mouth disease C) Frozen surface
   D) Waterlogged course

3) What separates the wins of Boldboy in 1977 and Markab in 2010 from all the other winners of the race?

4) The 2008 running of the race produced the last occasion when a French-trained horse won it. It was trained by Criquette Head-Maarek and ridden by Stephane Pasquier, but what was it called?

5) Colours have figured a few times among winners of the race. The Blues, Golden Orange and Red Clubs have all been successful, but one colour has appeared twice, in 1971 and 1986. The trainers were Michael Jarvis and Michael Stoute. Who were the two horses?

6) Kevin Darley has won the race twice this century riding for northern trainers, in 2000 on Pipalong and in 2006 on Reverence. Which two trainers were involved?

7) The most recent instance of a father-and-son combination landing the prize as trainer and jockey came in 2009. Who were the pair and which horse won the race?

8) A jockey who shared his surname with a Leeds United goalkeeper won the race for the only time on Tamarisk in 1998 for Roger Charlton and Highclere Racing. Who was he?

9) Runnett in 1981, Petong in 1984 and Sheikh Albadou in 1992 were all steered home by the same jockey. Who was he?

10) Which English trainer based in France won the Haydock Sprint Cup twice in the 1990s and then again in 2001?

Quiz No. 51

GROUP ONES – No. 5

THE INTERNATIONAL

VENUE – York / DISTANCE – 1m2f / FIRST RUN – 1972

1) Derby winner Roberto won the first running of the race in 1972 when it was known as the Benson & Hedges Gold Cup, beating Brigadier Gerard for the only time in his career. Who rode Roberto that afternoon at York?

2) Which horse, narrowly beaten by Shirley Heights in the 1978 Derby, gained some compensation when it won at York later in that year?

3) Three horses have won the race in successive seasons: the first for trainer Maurice Zilber in 1974 and 1975, the second for Michael Stoute in 1993 and 1994, and the third for Saeed bin Suroor in 1995 and 1996. Who are the three horses to achieve that double?

4) Two years after creating a stir by finishing second in Nashwan's Derby of 1989 at 500-1, Lady Beaverbrook's colt of seven letters landed what was now the Juddmonte International as a five-year-old for Michael Roberts and Clive Brittain in 1991. What was his name?

5) Only two jockeys have won the race three times in a row. Pat Eddery did it first in the 1980s, but who repeated the trick in the 1990s?

   A) Steve Cauthen B) Frankie Dettori C) Mick Kinane
   D) Walter Swinburn

6) Which two horses with countries for names have won the International this century?

7) Which jockey has been successful in the race for trainers Barry Hills, Patrick Biancone and David Elsworth?

8) Which father and son have both ridden the winner of the International?

9) Lester Piggott won the race five times and his last two wins in 1985 and 1992 were on horses that also won an English classic in the year they did so, the first afterwards and the second before. Who were the two horses?

10) Besides Steve Cauthen, who was the only other jockey born in the USA to win the International when he did so on Royal Anthem in 1999 for trainer Henry Cecil?

Quiz No. 52

GROUP ONES – No. 6
THE JULY CUP
VENUE – Newmarket / DISTANCE – 6f / FIRST RUN – 1876

1) Lester Piggott is the man for this race having won it ten times, but, more remarkably, in five different decades! Why was Tin Whistle's success for Lester in the 1960 renewal unique?

2) What did Sundridge do in the early years of the 20th century that no other horse has done in the July Cup?

3) The only French winner this century came in 2008 when which horse ridden by Davy Bonilla and trained by Freddy Head finished like a train up the rail to get up on the line?

4) Hayley Turner carved out her own piece of history in the 2011 July Cup when she became the first woman to ride the winner on Dream Ahead for which trainer?

5) Two of the greatest performances in the race came in the last year of the 20th century and two years later in 2001. Both were ridden by Mick Kinane and trained by Aidan O'Brien and they also have a musical connection. Who were the two horses?

6) Continuing with the musical theme, the 2001 winner for trainer Ed Walker and jockey Tom Marquand was a David Bowie song. Which one?

7) Let's make it a musical trio. The 1932 winner was something Beethoven wrote seven of, Brahms wrote four of, but Schubert drew a blank with. What was it called?

8) Lester Piggott and Vincent O'Brien combined to take the July Cup in 1973, 1978 and 1979. Solinus won the middle one, but if you add just three letters to the end of the 1973 winner you produce the 1979 winner. What were the two horses called?

9) The new millennium brought a new phenomenon to the ancient race when the prize went to Japan. The trainer was Hideyuki Mori and the jockey was Yutaka Take. What was the horse called?

10) In 2009 trainer Jeremy Noseda and jockey Tom Queally looked to have gotten their first July Cup win under their belt when their horse stormed clear entering the final furlong. However, as they sometimes will, it jinked violently right and they had to endure a few worrying seconds before the rail helped it to hold on. Which horse caused the alarm?

Quiz No. 53

GROUP ONES – No. 7
THE KING GEORGE VI & QUEEN ELIZABETH STAKES
VENUE – Ascot / DISTANCE – 1m 4f / FIRST RUN – 1951

1) Only two trainers have been successful in winning the King George three years running. The first did so between 1966 and 1968, while the second achieved the feat between 1997 and 1999. Who were the two trainers?

2) The Aga Khan was the winning owner in 2003 and again in 2005 when the race was run at Newbury. John Oxx trained both winners and they began with the same letter and also ended with the same letter. What were his two horses called?

3) The Queen's horses have been placed five times in the race named after her, the last time with a third-place finish in 2016. Which horse was placed in that race, trained by Michael Stoute, and what was the only horse she won the race with in 1954 after its second-place finish in the Derby in her coronation year?

4) The magnificent Enable upped the ante by landing a third King George in 2020. Previously only two horses had won the race twice. Who were they?

5) Which horse trained by Michael Stoute found one too good for it in both 2018 and 2019?

6) Living up to its name in the 1960 renewal, Aggressor, ridden by Jimmy Lindley, beat Petite Etoile and Lester Piggott. The trainer of the winner won the race once, but his son has won it five times up to 2021. Who trained Aggressor?

7) Two of the race's most brilliant winners toyed with opposition 30 years apart, the first in 1970 and the second in 2000. Who were they?

8) Sheikh Mohammed had consecutive winners in 1993 and 1994, one trained by Michael Stoute and the other by Henry Cecil, both of them making reference to a place you might visit for an evening's entertainment. What were they called?

9) Which colt, trained by Dick Hern and ridden by Willie Carson, lowered Oh So Sharp's colours in 1985 by beating her in the King George in a year which saw her complete the Triple Crown?

10) Before Enable in 2017, who was the last horse to win the Arc in the same year as winning the King George?

A) Danedream B) Dylan Thomas C) Hurricane Run D) Montjeu

Quiz No. 54

GROUP ONES – No. 8
THE LOCKINGE
VENUE – Newbury / DISTANCE – 1m / FIRST RUN – 1958

1) The Queen was the successful owner in the first two runnings of the Lockinge Stakes when her horse was trained by Cecil Boyd-Rochfort and ridden by WH Carr. As for the horse, he can be found on the Monopoly board. What was his name?

2) Apart from the aforementioned WH Carr, only two jockeys since have won the Lockinge in successive seasons, the first in 1968 and 1969 and the second in 2010 and 2011. They both begin with H. Who were they?

3) Richard Fahey became the first northern trainer to land the Lockinge since Captain Bill Elsey in 1978 when which horse won the 2017 renewal?

4) What did Ron Mason do in 1960 and Seamus McGrath repeat in 1967 that hasn't been done in all the other runnings of the race up to 2021?

5) Since the turn of the century three horses have won the Lockinge the year after they won an English Guineas. The Lockinge wins were in 2004, 2012 and 2015. The first of them won the 1,000 Guineas while the following two won the 2,000 Guineas. Who were the three horses?

6) For those old enough to remember, a dance group used to sometimes appear on BBC shows in the 1960s. They shared their name with the Guy Harwood-trained and Greville Starkey-ridden horse that won the Lockinge in 1979. What was it called?

7) Robert Armstrong and Lester Piggott teamed up to win the Lockinge in 1973 with a horse that's often seen on 5 November. What was its name?

8) Three Michaels have trained the winner of the race this century. Who are they?

9) Two landmarks found on the south coast of England, one man made and one not, have won the Lockinge this century. Which two horses are involved?

10) Both Richard Hannon Senior and Richard Hannon Junior have experienced back-to-back wins in the Lockinge this century. True or false?

Quiz No. 55

GROUP ONES – No. 9
THE NUNTHORPE
VENUE – York / DISTANCE – 5f / FIRST RUN – 1922

1) The Nunthorpe is a top prize that trainer John Gosden has captured just once up to 2021. He did so with which horse in 2003?

2) After three wins by juveniles in the 1950s and another in the 1990s, there has only been one instance of a two-year-old tasting victory in the race this century. It happened in 2007 with Kingsgate Native. Who played the jockey and trainer roles?

3) Going from the youngest to the oldest, which nine-year-old trained by Dandy Nicholls and ridden by Seb Sanders won the Nunthorpe in 2004?

4) What was unique about the back-to-back wins in the race of Robin Bastiman trained Borderlescott in 2008 and 2009?

5) Only two horses have won the race three times, and both of them did so successively. Tag End, trained by Charles Peck, did it between 1928 and 1930, but Sharpo, trained by Jeremy Tree, was the most recent to achieve the feat between 1980 and 1982. Which two jockeys were involved in Sharpo's success?

6) Only one horse has won the race and come back to repeat the feat four years later. The winning years were 2010 and 2014. Who was the horse?

7) Father-and-son team Barry and Michael Hills combined to take the Nunthorpe in 1988 with a horse owned by Robert Sangster, and then landed it again in 2005 for Guy Reed with a very fast filly. Who were their two winners?

8) The winners of the race in 1993 and 1998 were both trained by Ian Balding and ridden by Frankie Dettori for owner Jeff Smith. Another thing they had in common was the first four letters of their name. Who were the two horses, and, for a bonus point, the winner of the Nunthorpe in its first year of sponsorship by William Hill in 1976 also began with the same four letters. Who was it?

9) Which horse was runner-up in the race in 2003, 2004 and 2005?

A) Bishop's Court B) Dandy Man C) Malhub D) The Tatling

10) Up to 2021 who is the most recent trainer to have back-to-back winners of the Nunthorpe?

Quiz No. 56

GROUP ONES – No. 10
THE QUEEN ELIZABETH II STAKES
VENUE – Ascot / DISTANCE – 1m / FIRST RUN – 1955

1) Which jockey monopolised the race by winning it five times in six years between 1975 and 1980?

2) Frankie Dettori won the race in 1990 and 1996 on two horses that began with the same four letters, the second win constituting one of his 'magnificent seven'. Who were the two horses?

3) Hawk Wing had one of his off days in the 2002 race and succumbed to Where Or When, ridden by Kevin Darley and trained in Epsom by which man?

4) Which highly touted horse who flopped in Oath's Derby in 1999 showed that his build-up was well founded when turning in a superb performance to win that year's QEII as he pleased?

5) In another version of the 'Three Rs' and not as misleading as the educational one, the QEII was won in 2007, 2008 and 2009 by three horses beginning with that letter, trained by Saeed bin Suroor, John Gosden and Aidan O'Brien. Who were the talented trio?

6) Why would it have been more appropriate if the 1968 winner, trained by Paddy Prendergast and ridden by Bill Williamson, had won the 1966 version instead?

7) In the 66 runnings of the race up to 2021 no horse older than five has prevailed. True or false?

8) Up to 2021 only two trainers have won successive QEII's this century. John Gosden is one, but who is the other, whose wins came in 2014 and 2015?

9) Which jockey was successful in the race on board Air Express for Clive Brittain in 1997 and then returned the following year to win again with the David Loder-trained Desert Prince?

10) What is the link between the Fulke Johnson-Houghton-trained Romulus who won the 1962 edition of the race and the victory 20 years later of Buzzards Bay, trained by Hugh Collingridge?

Quiz No. 57

GROUP ONES – No. 11
THE ST. JAMES'S PALACE STAKES
VENUE – Royal Ascot / DISTANCE – 1m / FIRST RUN – 1834

1) After Black Tarquin had won the race in 1948 it was another 53 years before a horse with a colour in its name struck again. What was it called?

2) The very first race was a walk-over, but the second in 1835 was won by a horse with the perfect name for the job. What was it?

3) This race for three-year-old colts is often targeted by horses that have run in the 2,000 Guineas. In this century up to 2021, seven winners of the Newmarket event have gone on to win the St James's Palace Stakes at Royal Ascot. Three of them were trained by Aidan O'Brien, two by Jim Bolger and one each by Henry Cecil and Hugo Palmer. How many of the seven can you name?

4) Which politician won the race in 1863?

A) Disraeli B) Gladstone C) Palmerston D) Salisbury

5) Since the war, seven trainers with surnames starting with H have trained the winner of the St James's Palace Stakes. Alec Head did so for France in the 1960s, followed by Dick Hern in the 1970s, and in this century both Hannon's have done so. But which three managed it in the 1980s?

6) The magnificent Tudor Minstrel won the St James's Palace Stakes after an effortless canter in the 2,000 Guineas. If you had £100 on him with a bookie at Ascot how much would he have given you after the race?

7) Darryll Holland and Mick Channon teamed up to produce the only post-war winner of the race beginning with a Z in 2003 with which horse?

8) Merle Haggard sang 'I turned 21 in prison doing life _ _.' If you can fill in the gaps you will have the Frankie Dettori-ridden and John Gosden-trained winner of the 2018 edition of the St James's Palace Stakes. Can you?

9) In the first ten runnings of the race this century how many wins did Aidan O'Brien have as a trainer?

10) Which painter was successful in the 1937 running of the race?

A) Botticelli B) Goya C) Titian D) Velasquez

Quiz No. 58

GROUP ONES – No. 12
THE SUSSEX STAKES
VENUE – Goodwood / DISTANCE – 1m / FIRST RUN – 1878

1) Jockey Richard Hughes was successful on two horses for Richard Hannon Senior in the Sussex Stakes, the first in 2010 and the second in 2013. With which two horses?

2) Since the war only two fillies have gone on to win the Sussex Stakes after winning the 1,000 Guineas. Trained by Noel Murless and Peter Walwyn, they did so in 1959 and 1970. Who were they?

3) What is the link between the first six-year-old to win the Sussex Stakes, trained by Gavin Pritchard-Gordon and ridden by George Duffield in 1983, and the 2021 winner, trained by Andrew Balding and ridden by Oisin Murphy?

4) Which football club won the 1886 running of the Sussex Stakes?

   A) Arsenal B) Chelsea C) Portsmouth D) Southampton

5) The first seven-year-old winner came in 2017 with the connections being Andrew Balding and Jim Crowley, but, after all those years without one, another seven-year-old, trained by David Simcock and ridden by Oisin Murphy, won it in the very next year of 2018. Which two horses were involved?

6) The winner of the 1987 Sussex Stakes, trained by Andre Fabre and ridden by Greville Starkey, was the sire of the 2004 winner, trained by James Fanshawe and ridden by Johnny Murtagh. They shared the first word of their names and their initials. Who were they?

7) Which golf course was the victor in the 1895 edition of the race?

   A) Carnoustie B) St. Andrews C) Troon D) Wentworth

8) Between 1963 and 1966 which jockey won the Sussex Stakes three times on Queen's Hussar, Carlemont and Paveh?

A) Ron Hutchinson B) Geoff Lewis C) Lester Piggott
D) Bill Williamson

9) Which French philosopher won the race in 1937?

A) Descartes B) Pascal C) Rousseau D) Voltaire

10) Who was the only jockey to win the Sussex Stakes before and after World War Two, taking the race seven times in 11 runnings between 1936 and 1952?

Quiz No. 59

HISTORIC HANDICAPS –
No. 1 – THE AYR GOLD CUP
VENUE – Ayr / DISTANCE – 6f / FIRST RUN – 1804

1) This horse lived up to his name by winning the race three times between 1889 and 1891. What was that name?

   A) Brilliance B) Dazzle C) Superstar D) Threefold

2) Which two Hollywood stars won the race in 2010 and 2016?

3) After coming second in 2013, which horse, trained by David O'Meara and ridden by James Doyle, went one better the following year?

4) Another horse to go one better the next year was this one, trained by Richard Fahey and ridden by Paul Hanagan, who won the race in 2006. Who was he?

5) Who were the only two trainers to win the race twice in the 1990s? The horses involved were Lochsong, Grangeville, Daring Destiny and Always Alight.

6) An early career win for Oisin Murphy came in the 2013 renewal of the race on a horse trained by Andrew Balding. What was its name?

7) Which horse, trained by David Barron and ridden by Jimmy Fortune, followed up his win in the Stewards Cup by taking this prize as well in 1996?

8) Which two trainers have farmed the race between them in this century, landing it 11 times in 22 runnings?

9) The only dead-heat since the war was between the 5-1 favourite Son of Rest and 28 1 chance Baron Bolt. In which year was it?

10) The two Kevins, Ryan and Stott, were the connections when which football manager won the Ayr Gold Cup in 2021?

Quiz No. 60

HISTORIC HANDICAPS –
No. 2 – THE CAMBRIDGESHIRE
VENUE – Newmarket / DISTANCE – 1m 1f / FIRST RUN – 1839

1) Since the war, who is the only trainer to win back-to-back editions of the Cambridgeshire, and, just for good measure, he has performed the feat twice?

2) When Liam Keniry and David Elsworth combined to take the 2004 Cambridgeshire with Spanish Don it was returned the biggest-priced winner since Pullover in 1932. What was its price?

3) Which horse trained by Frankie Durr and ridden by Peter Robinson became the only horse to land the race in the 1960s and 1970s when it was successful two years running in 1969 and 1970?

4) This horse was a standing dish in the race when, trained by John Benstead and piloted by Brian Rouse, he won both the 1978 and 1980 renewals and twice finished second into the bargain. Who was he?

5) Which planet won the race under Gordon Richards in 1953?

   A) Jupiter B) Mercury C) Neptune D) Saturn

6) Who is the only trainer to send out the winner of the Cambridgeshire in the 1980s, the 1990s and the 2000s?

   A) David Elsworth B) Jeremy Glover C) Barry Hills
   D) Mark Prescott

7) Which jockey, who shared his name with a well-known darts player of the time, won the race with Leysh in 1984 and Mellottie in 1991?

8) Which jockey, who won on Smartset in 1979, went through the 1980s and 1990s without troubling the judges before landing the race again in 2000 with Katy Nowaitee?

9) Referencing a fictitious boxer, which horse, trained by Jeremy Glover and ridden by Dean McKeown, was the only horse to win the Cambridgeshire in the 1980s and 1990s?

10) Which trainer's Bronze Angel was twice successful in the race in 2012 and 2014?

Quiz No. 61

HISTORIC HANDICAPS –
No. 3 – THE CESAREWITCH
VENUE – Newmarket / DISTANCE – 2m 2f / FIRST RUN – 1839

1) This October staying contest known as the second leg of the 'autumn double' was captured on ten occasions between 1935 and 1966 by two jockeys who were brothers. Who were they?

2) Jumps trainer Philip Hobbs teamed up with jockey Tom Queally to take the 2014 Cesarewitch with a horse who could have been named after golfer Ernie Els. What was it called?

3) Who was the only jockey to win the race in the 1960s, 1970s and 1980s, doing so on Major Rose, John Cherry and Popsi's Joy?

4) Who are the only two jockeys this century to claim back-to-back wins in the Cesarewitch?

5) Since the war, two female trainers have taken the prize: the first with Double Dutch in 1989, and the second with both Old Red in 1995 and Turnpole in 1997. Who are the two women?

6) Who is the only trainer since the war to have won the race three years running?

7) Jockey Nicky Carlisle, if his name is anything to go by, took his equine partner's advice when going to Newmarket to land the Cesarewitch for trainer John Jenkins in 1991. What was the winner called?

8) Up to 2021 which trainer has won the race three times with Spirit of Love in 1998, Contact Dancer in 2004 and Scatter Dice in 2013?

9) Up to 2021 big-race jockey Frankie Dettori has just one win to his name in the race. It came for trainer Jamie Osborne in 2011 on which horse?

10) Which 1992 winner of the race for Walter Swinburn and Dermot Weld went on to win successive Irish St Legers?

Quiz No. 62

HISTORIC HANDICAPS –
No. 4 – THE CHESTER CUP
VENUE – Chester / DISTANCE – 2m 2f / FIRST RUN – 1824

1) Trainer Mark Johnston finally broke his duck in the Chester Cup when taking it in 2019 with support from Chester specialist Franny Norton. Which horse lived up to his name?

2) Owner Marwan Koukash loves having a winner at this track, so it's no surprise that he's won the Chester Cup four times, in 2008, 2013, 2014 and 2018. The winning jockeys were Jim Crowley, Jamie Spencer, Ryan Moore and Fran Berry. Which four horses were they successful on?

3) Something you usually take from the doctors to the chemists won the 1955 running of the Chester Cup for jockey Bill Rickaby and trainer Jack Jarvis. What was it called?

4) Which horse had back-to-back wins in the race in 2004 and 2005, the first as a 2-1 favourite and the second at 16-1 for trainer Michael Jarvis and jockey Philip Robinson?

5) Which Barry Hills-trained horse, ridden on the first occasion by Michael Hills, and on the second by Richard Hughes, is the only one to win the Chester Cup in both the 20th and 21st centuries?

6) Trainer Lynda Ramsden and jockey Alan Munro won the 1990 renewal of the Chester Cup with a horse that despite its name was still carrying over 9st on the day. What was it called?

7) Which jockey commonly known as 'Flapper' won successive Chester Cups in 1962 and 1963 with Golden Fire and Narratus?

8) Willie Carson's two wins in the race came in 1979 and 1985, firstly for trainer Bill Wightman, and then for owner/trainer John Hill. The two horses shared the same word in their names. What were they called?

9) Which Indian tribe provided jockey Steve Cauthen with his sole win in the race in 1980 for trainer Barry Hills?

10) Which jockey won the race on Trelawney in 1960, Harvest Gold in 1965 and Random Shot in 1971?

A) Paul Cook B) Frankie Durr C) Geoff Lewis D) Lester Piggott

Quiz No. 63

HISTORIC HANDICAPS – No. 5 – THE EBOR
VENUE – York / DISTANCE – 1m 6f / FIRST RUN – 1843

1) It was a top-class winner of the Ebor in 1958 when that year's Ascot Gold Cup winner took the race for trainer Vincent O'Brien and jockey Lester Piggott. Which filly won the race?

2) Who was the only jockey to win the race in the 1940s, 1950s and 1960s?

   A) Edgar Britt B) Lester Piggott C) Bill Rickaby D) Joe Sime

3) One jockey had successive wins in the race in the 1960s on Ovaltine and Alignment, while another did the same in the 1970s on Knotty Pine and Crazy Rhythm. Which two jockeys were involved?

4) He won the Ebor in 1984 on Crazy for Guy Harwood, and his father won it exactly 30 years earlier on By Thunder for trainer Fred Armstrong. What family name are we looking for here?

5) Which three female trainers have won the Ebor this century, in 2000, 2006 and 2013, with Give the Slip, Mudawin and Tiger Cliff respectively?

6) Which legendary horse over both codes became the only nine-year-old winner of the race since the war when taking it in 1979?

7) Paul Eddery in 1988 on Kneller and Kieren Fallon on Tuning a decade later have both won the Ebor for which trainer?

8) Up to 2021, only one trainer has saddled the winner of the Ebor in both the 20th and 21st centuries, landing it in 1999, 2004 and 2007. Who was he?

9) Only one jockey up to 2021 has won the race twice this century. Who is it?

   A) Andrea Atzeni B) Frankie Dettori C) Tom Queally
   D) Jamie Spencer

10) The 2008 running of the race was won by All the Good for trainer Saeed bin Suroor and jockey Dane O'Neill, but didn't take place at York. Where was the race held that year?

Quiz No. 64

HISTORIC HANDICAPS – No. 6 – THE LINCOLN
VENUE – Doncaster / DISTANCE – 1m / FIRST RUN – 1853

1) In the five years between 1997 and 2001, which trainer produced three winners of this curtain raiser to the flat season in Kuala Lipis, John Ferneley and Nimello?

2) The winner of the 1867 Lincoln shared his name with someone who took his shoes and socks off and went for a dip in the Barry Burn at Carnoustie in the 1999 Open Golf Championship. What was it called?

3) Since the race was moved from Lincoln to Doncaster in 1965 only one man has trained four winners of the race up to 2021. The horses were High Low, Very Wise, Penitent and Addeybb. Who was that trainer?

4) In the last Lincoln of the 20th century a political expression trained by John Dunlop and ridden by Richard Quinn was the winning favourite, looking like a group horse in a handicap. What was it called?

5) The first two winners of the race at Doncaster in 1965 and 1966 were Old Tom and Riot Act. They were ridden by the same jockey. Who?

A) Scobie Breasley B) Eddie Hide C) Lester Piggott D) Doug Smith

6) Who became, up to 2021, the only woman to ride a Lincoln winner when getting home on Amenable in 1991 for David Barron?

7) How are the boardgames company Waddingtons linked to the Lincoln?

8) With just a two-letter name, which horse won back-to-back Lincolns in 1906 and 1907?

A) AB B) EB C) IB D) OB

9) The first Irish-trained winner since the move to Doncaster came in 1984 when Walter Swinburn steered home Saving Mercy. Who saddled it?

10) Frankincense's victory in 1968 for trainer John Oxley and jockey Greville Starkey had a much wider significance for one man. Who and why?

Quiz No. 65

HISTORIC HANDICAPS –
No. 7 – THE NORTHUMBERLAND PLATE
VENUE – Newcastle / DISTANCE – 2m / FIRST RUN – 1833

1) By what name is the race sometimes referred to by locals?

2) Owner Marwan Koukash had the winner and the second in the 2014 renewal. Suegioo was the runner-up, but which horse claimed the prize?

3) Far Cry was the victor for trainer Martin Pipe in the last 20th-century running of the Northumberland Plate, while the first winner of the 21st century was Bay of Islands for David Morris. One jockey was successful on both of them. Who was he?

4) Only one horse has won the race three times, and did so in successive years in 1857, 1858 and 1859. Who was the horse, whose name suggests it wasn't all above board?

5) The only horse this century up to 2021 to win the race twice did so in 2011 and 2013 under two different trainers; firstly with a flat trainer and then with a jumps trainer. Who was the horse?

6) Since the war there has only been one occasion when jockeys with the same first names followed one another as winners of the Northumberland Plate. This happened in 2014 and 2015. Who were the two jockeys?

7) Who are the only two trainers to win the race in both the 20th and 21st centuries, the first of them doing so with victories in 1997, 1998 and 2001, while the second, after winning it in 1995, had to wait until 2017 before doing so again?

8) I backed this horse at Ascot when it won in May 2006, but wished I had stuck with it when it won the Northumberland Plate as well at 33-1, ridden by Nelson de Souza and trained by George M Moore. Who was it?

9) Which jockey had a 28-year gap between his first win in the race for trainer Bernard Van Cutsem in 1968 and his last one for David Morley in 1996, and also won it in 1990 for Alec Stewart?

10) Trained by Dermot Whelan and ridden by Brian Rouse, this tough stayer won the race two years in a row in 1977 and 1978 and is something you might see at a fete. What was he called?

Quiz No. 66

HISTORIC HANDICAPS –
No. 8 – THE PORTLAND
VENUE – Doncaster / DISTANCE – 5f 140 yards / FIRST RUN – 1855

1) A lot of Hs here! Owned by Hamdan al Maktoum, trained by William Haggas and ridden by Paul Hanagan, which horse won the 2014 Portland at 3-1, the shortest-priced winner since 1969?

2) Kieren Fallon won the race on Astonished in 1999. Then, exactly 20 years later, his son Cieren won it too, on board which horse for trainer Roger Teal?

3) The 2006 edition of the race took place at York and was won by Fantasy Believer. Another rarity was that the trainer and jockey shared the same surname. What was it?

4) Adam Kirby and Clive Cox combined to take the 2005 running of the race with a horse that sounds like what people are likely to be on Halloween or Bonfire Night! What was it called?

5) After finishing third in 2006, this horse, trained by Stuart Williams and piloted by Saleem Golam, came back two years later to land the Portland. Its name has Scottish connections. What was it?

6) Which trainer equalled his father's record in the race with Angels Will Fall in 2013, before going on to pass him with A Moment of Madness in 2018?

7) Between 2009 and 2012 the Portland winner was trained by three Davids. The successful horses were Santo Padre, Poet's Place, Nocturnal Affair and Doc Hay. Who were the three trainers?

8) Which jockey completed a double in the race on Musical Season in 1996 and Dashing Blue in 1997?

9) Hello Mister completed a double in the race for trainer Jack O'Donoghue and jockey Pat McCabe in the middle of which decade?

10) Which horse and trainer uniquely won the race three times in a row between 2002 and 2004?

Quiz No. 67

HISTORIC HANDICAPS –
No. 9 – THE ROYAL HUNT CUP
VENUE – Royal Ascot / DISTANCE – 1m / FIRST RUN – 1843

1) Martin Dwyer and Amanda Perrett teamed up to win the 2017 Hunt Cup with the first horse beginning with a Z to do so since Zaleucus in 1964. Who was the horse?

2) Jockey Gary Bardwell and trainer David Elsworth combined to score with Pontenuovo in 1990 in what was the biggest SP of the Hunt Cup winner since 1955. What was the SP of the 1990 winner?

3) The Queen won the race twice in the 1950s, but had to wait until 1992 for her next win when which horse, trained by Lord Huntingdon and ridden by David Harrison, took the race for her?

4) Which Hunt Cup winner for trainer Reg Akehurst and jockey Alan Munro in 1994 imitates a compass?

5) Kamundu, who won the 1969 renewal for Lester Piggott and trainer Frank Carr, shares a characteristic with Field of Dream, victorious in 2014 for Adam Kirby and Jamie Osborne, that no other post-war winner shares. What is it?

6) Since the distance of the race was changed in 1930 the shortest-priced winner was returned at 4-1 when Forgotten Voice did the business under Johnny Murtagh in 2009. Who trained the winner?

7) Who is the only trainer to win the Hunt Cup in the 1970s, 1980s and 1990s?

   A) Henry Cecil B) John Dunlop C) Barry Hills D) Michael Stoute

8) Three jockeys up to 2021 have won the race twice this century. Which one of these four hasn't done so?

   A) Frankie Dettori B) James Doyle C) Jimmy Fortune
   D) Johnny Murtagh

9) What was it about Afaak's win in the 2019 edition of the race that hadn't happened in the 21st century before?

10) Who became the only man since the war with a three-letter surname to train a winner of the Hunt Cup when New Seeker obliged in 2005?

Quiz No. 68

HISTORIC HANDICAPS –
No. 10 – THE STEWARDS' CUP
VENUE – Goodwood / DISTANCE – 6f / FIRST RUN – 1840

1) Trainer John Scott shares with James Jewitt the most wins in the Stewards' Cup with a total of four. In 1853 he won the race with a weapon that was crucial to the English winning at Agincourt in 1415. What was his horse called?

2) Up to 2021 the last trainer to saddle successive Stewards' Cup winners did so with Knight of Mercy in 1990 and Notley in 1991, both at 14-1. Who was he?

3) The 2005 winner for Dandy Nicholls and Kieren Fallon and the 2018 winner for Hugo Palmer and Jason Watson share the first four letters of their names. What were the two horses called?

4) Which jockey, having already been successful in the race on Dunme in 1964, collected back-to-back wins in 1972 and 1973 with Touch Paper and Alphadamus?

5) Which famous painter won the 1960 renewal with Jeremy Tree doing the training and Jimmy Lindley the steering?

A) Cezanne B) Monet C) Picasso D) Raphael

6) In 1988 a village two miles west of Henley-on-Thames in Oxfordshire gave trainer Chris Wall and jockey Nigel Day their only success in the race. What was the horse called?

7) Who rode the winner of a Stewards' Cup in the 1980s, drew a blank in the 1990s, but returned with a vengeance to train three winners of the race in the new century?

8) Up to 2021 who is the only trainer to have won the Stewards' Cup in both the 20th and 21st centuries?

A) Roger Charlton B) John Gosden C) Peter Makin
D) Michael Stoute

9) Which is the only surname to appear twice among winning trainers in the Stewards' Cup this century?

10) When Red Alert won the race in 1974 he was the first horse with a colour in his name to do so since the second world war. But 12 years later a horse with two colours in his name was a 20-1 winner for trainer Toby Balding. What was it called?

Quiz No. 69

HISTORIC HANDICAPS –
No. 11 – THE VICTORIA CUP
VENUE – Ascot / DISTANCE – 7f / FIRST RUN – 1908

1) Which trainer won this early-season handicap three times in the 1990s, in 1991, 1994 and 1997?

   A) Reg Akehurst B) Ian Balding C) Michael Jarvis
   D) Dandy Nicholls

2) Female jockeys were responsible for successive winners of the race in 2017 and 2018 when Fastnet Tempest and Ripp Orf took the prize. Which two jockeys rode those Victoria Cup winners?

3) Which jockey won back-to-back Victoria Cups in 1973 and 1974 on Royal Prerogative for Denys Smith and Galiano for Barry Hills?

4) I don't like horses being given the same name as an earlier one that's relatively well known. Half a century, give or take a year, after the 1954 Victoria Cup winner, a horse with the same name won the Cambridgeshire for Mark Prescott and George Duffield. What was the name both horses went by?

5) Up to 2021, the last Victoria Cup winner with an X in its name won the 1990 race under Pat Eddery for Guy Harwood. It might have been named for a collector of examples of the blues from the American south, but then again it might not! What was it called?

6) The Victoria Cup had to be moved from Ascot for one season in 2005. Where was it run?

   A) Goodwood B) Haydock Park C) Lingfield Park D) Sandown Park

7) When Kenny Gethin piloted Petition to victory in the race in 1948 it seemed unlikely that the horse would land any of the following big races before the season was over, but he did. Which one?

   A) The Eclipse B) The St. James's Palace Stakes C) The Sussex Stakes
   D) The 2,000 Guineas

1,000 QUESTIONS ON HORSERACING

8) Who was the only jockey to win the Victoria Cup twice in the 1990s with Band On The Run and Tragaron?

9) Which four members of the same family have won the race as jockey or trainer this century?

10) When Speculative Bid won the 2015 renewal, the horse in second place, trained by Mick Channon and ridden by Charles Bishop, had a name that was another historic handicap of a similar distance. What was it called?

Quiz No. 70

HISTORIC HANDICAPS –
No.12 – THE WOKINGHAM
VENUE – Royal Ascot / DISTANCE – 6f / FIRST RUN – 1813

1) Four horses have won this ancient race twice, the first of them doing so in 1881 and 1882. It had an appropriate name. What was it?

2) How are Tayr Jag, ridden by Willie Supple and trained by Tim Easterby, and Ratio, ridden by Frankie Dettori and trained by John Hammond, connected in the history of the race?

3) Since the war, five jockeys have won back-to-back Wokinghams. Who was, up to 2021, the last to do so on Laddies Poker Two in 2010 and Deacon Blues in 2011?

4) In 2005 Michael Jarvis trained the shortest-priced winner of the race since the war when which horse ridden by Philip Robinson won at 9-4?

5) Which father-and-son trained Wokingham winners in the 1990s, the father with Emerging Market in 1996 and the son with Deep Space in 1999?

6) In 2016 and 2017 successive Wokingham winners shared the opening three letters of their names, one of them trained by Robert Cowell and the other by David O'Meara. Who were the two horses?

7) The 2013 winner's name, when his connections were Kevin Ryan and Jamie Spencer, referenced another racecourse where the race took place eight years before. What was the winner called?

8) Astrac won the Wokingham in 1995 under Pat Eddery, and in the new century, in 2002, Capricho did the same with Richard Quinn in the saddle. Who were the trainers of those winners and what is the relationship between them?

9) The 1961 winner for jockey Joe Sime and trainer Sam Hall was the offspring of a famous painter. What was it called?

A) Blake's Babe B) Constable's Child C) Son of Stubbs
D) Whistler's Daughter

10) The only country to win the Wokingham did so in 1939 and is also a rock band and a novel by Franz Kafka. What was it called?

Quiz No. 71
HORSES FOR COURSES

1) Which sprinter trained by Ruth Carr won eight times at Ripon between 2013 and 2018?

2) Which horse trained by John Spearing has now got his own race at Beverley after winning there 12 times between 1983 and 1989?

3) Which Arthur Stephenson-trained horse was a standing dish at Wetherby, winning nine times in either chases or hurdles races at the track between 1967 and 1974?

4) Which horse trained by Richard Hannon Senior had seven of his eight career wins at Newmarket between May 2006 and July 2009?

5) Which grey trained by Barry Hills won five successive Jockey Club Cups at Newmarket between 1991 and 1995?

6) Which horse trained by Tony Carroll has won 11 times at Brighton between 2013 and 2021?

7) Which horse, arguably the most exciting jumper of them all, loved Sandown Park where he ran in the Sandown Pattern Chase six years running in the 1970s and was never out of the front two, winning it three times and breaking the course record each time before having a big race at the track named in his honour?

8) Which David Barker-trained horse knows almost as much about Pontefract as Norman Gundill, having run there 36 times, winning on eight occasions between 2005 and 2010?

9) Which front-running chaser, trained in Kent by Albert Neaves, won 14 times at Fontwell Park between 1959 and 1966?

10) The summer of 1976 was a bit on the warm side and Brighton was like a road. Which fast ground specialist trained by the handicap king Reg Akehurst took advantage of the situation to rattle up five wins on the track that summer?

Quiz No. 72

THE IRISH DERBY

1) Only one horse completed the English and Irish Derby double in the 1960s. Who was it?

   A) Charlottown B) Santa Claus C) Sir Ivor D) St. Paddy

2) Who was the last horse to win the Irish Derby and the Arc in the same season and since then, which is the only horse in this century to win both races, but not in the same season?

3) Troy in 1979 and Zagreb in 1996 were winning cities in the Irish Derby. Up to 2021, which is the only other city to have been successful in the race?

4) Up to 2021 which four jockeys have won back-to-back Irish Derbys in this century?

5) Who are the only three non-Irish men to train the winner of the Irish Derby this century up to 2021?

6) It is a race that Frankie Dettori has won just once, in 1994, on which horse?

7) The Aga Khan, up to 2021, has won the Irish Derby six times between 1981 and 2016 with four different trainers. Who are they?

8) Trained by Paddy Prendergast and ridden by Jimmy Mullane, which horse won the race in 1952?

   A) Thirteen of Clubs B) Thirteen of Diamonds C) Thirteen of Hearts D) Thirteen of Spades

9) Who rode Shergar when he won the Irish Derby in 1981?

10) Who was the shortest-priced winning favourite in the Irish Derby this century?

   A) Australia B) Camelot C) Galileo D) High Chaparral

Quiz No. 73

THE JOCKEYS' CHAMPIONSHIP – THE FLAT

1) Which two jockeys whose surnames start with the same letter won five titles between them between 2010 and 2014?

2) In which year did Ryan Moore last win the jockeys' title?

3) In 1979, 1992 and 2000 which three jockeys were champions for the only time in their careers?

4) Which legendary jockey was champion 13 times in a row between 1874 and 1886?

5) The highest total of winners in a season is 269. Which of the following achieved it?

   A) Frankie Dettori B) Kieren Fallon C) Lester Piggott D) Gordon Richards

6) The surname of the winner of the first three flat jockeys' titles in 1850, 1851 and 1852 was very appropriate. What was it?

   A) Flatman B) Paddock C) Rider D) Silk

7) No jockey has won the title in four different decades. True or false?

8) Only two men with a first name starting with O have been champion jockey. One's easy and the other is hard. Who were they?

9) Who are the only two jockeys to win the title in two different millennia?

10) There have been four occasions when the jockeys' title has been shared. Which two riders were involved the last time this happened in 2007?

Quiz No. 74

THE JOCKEYS' CHAMPIONSHIP – THE JUMPS

1) Why is Jack Anthony unique among winners of the championship?

2) Without the existence of AP McCoy, how many times would Richard Johnson have been champion jockey?

   A) 19 B) 20 C) 21 D) 22

3) Who was the only jockey to win the title either side of World War Two?

A) Jack Dowdeswell B) Frenchie Nicholson C) Fred Rimell D) Ron Smyth

4) It is unlikely that AP McCoy's total of 20 wins will ever be matched, but who stands in second place with a total of eight wins to his name?

   A) John Francome B) Tim Molony C) Peter Scudamore
   D) Gerry Wilson

5) Who was the only jockey before World War Two to reach 100 winners in a season when he did so in 1924?

   A) Jack Anthony B) Ted Leader C) Fred Rees D) Billy Stott

6) Which occupation won the title six times in seven years between 1901 and 1907?

   A) Butler B) Carter C) Cook D) Mason

7) Which jockey in 1988/89 became the first to record over 200 winners in a season?

8) In the 11 seasons between 1927/28 and 1937/38 the title was in the hands of just two jockeys. Who were they?

9) Which Welsh town won the jockeys' championship in 1972/73 and 1973/74?

10) If you double the number of winners AP McCoy achieved in the lowest total in his 20 titles it still doesn't reach the number he achieved in his best season. True or false?

Quiz No. 75

MISSING INGREDIENTS – No. 1 – HORSES

You are given the year, the name of the race, the trainer and the jockey. What is missing is the horse. Who is it in each instance?

1) 2018   2,000 Guineas   Aidan O'Brien   Donacha O'Brien

2) 2016   Derby   Dermot Weld   Pat Smullen

3) 1996   1,000 Guineas   Henry Cecil   Pat Eddery

4) 2004   Oaks   Ed Dunlop   Kieren Fallon

5) 2002   St Leger   Tim Easterby   Kevin Darley

6) 2008   Grand National   David Pipe   Timmy Murphy

7) 1996   Champion Hurdle   Jim Old   Graham Bradley

8) 2000   Gold Cup   Noel Chance   Richard Johnson

9) 2012   Queen Mother Champion Chase   Nicky Henderson   Barry Geraghty

10) 2001   King George VI Chase   Willie Mullins   Adrian Maguire

Quiz No. 76

MISSING INGREDIENTS – No. 2 – TRAINERS

You are given the year, the name of the race, the horse and the jockey. What is missing is the trainer. Who is it in each instance?

1) 1980   2,000 Guineas   Known Fact   Willie Carson

2) 2006   Derby   Sir Percy   Martin Dwyer

3) 1986   1,000 Guineas   Midway Lady   Ray Cochrane

4) 2005   Oaks   Eswarah   Richard Hills

5) 2006   St Leger   Sixties Icon   Frankie Dettori

6) 2014   Grand National   Pineau De Re   Leighton Aspell

7) 1997   Champion Hurdle   Make A Stand   AP McCoy

8) 2015   Gold Cup   Coneygree   Nico de Boinville

9) 2010   Queen Mother Champion Chase   Big Zeb   Barry Geraghty

10) 1998   King George VI Chase   Teeton Mill   Norman Williamson

Quiz No. 77

MISSING INGREDIENTS – No. 3 – JOCKEYS

You are given the year, the name of the race, the horse and the trainer. What is missing is the jockey. Who is it in each instance?

1) 1991   2,000 Guineas   Mystiko   Clive Brittain

2) 2017   Derby   Wings of Eagles   Aidan O'Brien

3) 2008   1,000 Guineas   Natagora   Pascal Bary

4) 2010   Oaks   Snow Fairy   Ed Dunlop

5) 2007   St Leger   Lucarno   John Gosden

6) 2001   Grand National   Red Marauder   Norman Mason

7) 2007   Champion Hurdle   Sublimity   John Carr

8) 2006   Gold Cup   War of Attrition   Michael Morris

9) 2002   Queen Mother Champion Chase   Flagship Uberalles   Philip Hobbs

10) 1993   King George VI Chase   Barton Bank   David Nicholson

Quiz No. 78

MISSING INGREDIENTS – No. 4 – THE YEAR

You are given the name of the race, the horse, the trainer and the jockey. What is missing is the year. What is it in each instance?

1) 2,000 Guineas   Rock of Gibraltar   Aidan O'Brien   Johnny Murtagh

2) Derby   Secreto   David O'Brien   Christy Roche

3) 1,000 Guineas   Sky Lantern   Richard Hannon Senior   Richard Hughes

4) Oaks   Oh So Sharp   Henry Cecil   Steve Cauthen

5) St Leger   Arctic Cosmos   John Gosden   William Buick

6) Grand National   Papillon   Ted Walsh   Ruby Walsh

7) Champion Hurdle   Brave Inca   Colm Murphy   AP McCoy

8) Gold Cup   Mill House   Fulke Walwyn   Willie Robinson

9) Queen Mother Champion Chase   Dodging Bullets   Paul Nicholls   Sam Twiston-Davies

10) King George VI Chase   Thistlecrack   Colin Tizzard   Tom Scudamore

Quiz No. 79

MISSING WORDS

Enter a new word in the space to produce two horses in each case, e.g.
Midway (Lady) Carla produces Midway Lady, winner of the 1,000 Guineas
and Lady Carla, winner of the Oaks.

All the horses involved have won big races at home or abroad on the flat
since the 1960s.

(1)   English   (   )   Bishop

(2)   Fancy   (   )   Wind

(3)   Holding   (   )   Masterpiece

(4)   Spanish   (   )   Ballad

(5)   Royal   (   )   Pier

(6)   Rainbow   (   )   Rise

(7)   Snow   (   )   Footsteps

(8)   Urban   (   )   Pigeon

(9)   Thunder   (   )   Knight

(10)   Fighting   (   )   Bubbles

Quiz No. 80

'OH, I DO LIKE TO BE BESIDE THE SEASIDE'
BRIGHTON RACES

You could say I've rocked up at Brighton more times than at any other racecourse. Here are some questions about that idiosyncratic track.

1) In August 1987 which foreign jockey secured his 1,000th winner in Britain at Brighton aboard Henry Cecil's Picnicing?

2) Who became the first northern trainer to reach 100 winners in a flat season for 58 years when Heaven-Leigh-Grey won a Brighton nursery in August 1990?

3) Arguably the greatest horse to run at the track, she won successive Brighton Challenge Cups in 1967 and 1968 in a career that included a Ribblesdale, Hardwicke and King George at Ascot, an Epsom Coronation Cup and second place in the Arc. Who was she?

4) Sprinter Shakiri's Son rattled up nine wins on the track early on in his career before landing which big handicap race as an eight-year-old in 1995?

5) Which jockey opened his Brighton account with Star of Clubs on 10 August 1950?

6) The Queen won the Brighton Trophy two years in a row in 1992 and 1993 with Talent and Set the Fashion. One man trained them both. Who was he? (Clever horse that One Man!)

7) In October 2001 what happened to the favourite Dodona and rider Kieren Fallon at the start for the 4.40 race?

8) In June 1977 an owner of extreme wealth won under £1,000 when he had his first winner in this country at Brighton with Hatta, trained by John Dunlop and ridden by Ron Hutchinson. Who was he?

9) Which Dick Hern-trained horse won the Brighton Derby trial in 1962, was brought down in the Derby, but went on to win the St Leger?

10) Which jockey, on 27 April 2008, rode a four-timer at the track?

A) Neil Callan B) Richard Hills C) Richard Quinn D) Seb Sanders

Quiz No. 81

OWNERS – FLAT RACING

1) Who was leading owner for the first time in 1954 before becoming so again in 1957?

2) Who was the only man to be leading owner in the 1920s, 1930s, 1940s and 1950s?

3) Who became leading owner through the exploits of the magnificent Sea The Stars?

4) Who was the first to reach a million pounds when he became leading owner in 1985?

5) Which Doctor has thus far been the only one to be leading owner when he also became, in 1975, the first to reach £200,000?

6) The last two female winners of the leading owner tag were in 2008 and 1972. Who were they?

7) Who was the only man to be leading owner in both the 1970s and 1980s?

8) The leading owner in both 1973 and 1974 has a name that's a combination of a naval hero, a golf hazard and a motor-racing world champion. What was his name?

9) Which owner, who could consider himself unlucky not to have landed the 1986 Derby, put that right four years later?

10) Which owners were associated with the following four Derby-winning horses?

A) Nijinsky B) Slip Anchor C) Reference Point D) Nashwan

Quiz No. 82

OWNERS – JUMPS RACING

1) The owner of the great dual Grand National winner of 1935 and 1936, Reynoldstown, was a measure of distance. What was his surname?

   A) Foot B) Furlong C) Miles D) Yard

2) Anne, Duchess of Westminster, will forever be associated with Arkle, but which other horse did she win the Cheltenham Gold Cup with in 1975?

3) Lutteur III won the 1909 Grand National, Mandarin won the 1962 Cheltenham Gold Cup, and Sublimity won the 2007 Champion Hurdle. All three owners had the same surname. What was it?

4) Which comedian owned Miinnehoma, winner of the 1994 Grand National?

5) Trevor Hemmings was a popular figure at the racecourse and was rewarded with three winners of the Grand National. Who were they?

6) The Dikler won the Cheltenham Gold Cup in 1973 and the owner of that horse had a month for a name. What was it?

   A) August B) January C) March D) May

7) After numerous attempts, holiday camp owner Fred Pontin finally landed the Grand National with which horse in 1971?

8) The owner of Punjabi, the Champion Hurdle hero of 2009, had a part of the body for his surname. What was it?

9) Pendil and Captain Christy captured back-to-back King George VI Chases, the former in 1972 and 1973, and the latter in 1974 and 1975. They were owned by two married women whose surnames both began with S, the first a bird and the second a book of the Bible. Who were they?

10) JP McManus has been a dominant figure among owners of jumps horses for many years, and has enjoyed a particular affinity with the Champion Hurdle. Up to 2021, how many times has he been successful in that race?

Quiz No. 83

PIGGOTT PUZZLERS

1) Which Yorkshire football ground did Lester win races on at Epsom, Goodwood, Sandown and York in 1976 and 1977?

   A) Bramall Lane B) Elland Road C) Hillsborough D) Oakwell

2) On 4 July 1961 which magazine was Lester successful on at Nottingham?

   A) *Hello* B) *Private Eye* C) *The Spectator* D) *Vogue*

3) In 1964 at Haydock Park and in the following year at Newbury Lester won for trainer Fulke Johnson – Houghton on a sprinter that shares its name with a Dire Straits song. Was it:

   A) Brothers In Arms B) Money for Nothing C) Telegraph Road
   D) Tunnel Of Love

4) On 17 June 1965 Lester rode a treble at Royal Ascot on Fighting Charlie, Swift Harmony and Brave Knight. Nothing unusual in that. What was unusual, however, was that they all started at the same price. Was it:

   A) 4-1 B) 6-1 C) 8-1 D) 10-1

5) Which Clint Eastwood film did Lester win on at Newmarket over five furlongs for trainer Robert Armstrong on 23 August 1974?

   A) Klute B) Magnum Force C) Unforgiven D) Where Eagles Dare

6) In September 1956 Lester won twice at Salisbury and Windsor on a horse that shares its name with an American President. Was it:

   A) Eisenhower B) Kennedy C) Nixon D) Trump

7) On 25 August 1980 Lester had a winner at Newcastle on a horse that shares its name with a rock group. Was it:

   A) Cream B) Roxy Music C) Mott the Hoople D) Procol Harum

8) On 1 May 1965 at Ascot, Lester won on a horse called Anselmo, trained by his father Keith, which went on to finish fourth in the Derby won by Santa Claus. Which pop singer owned it?

    A) Tommy Steele B) Cliff Richard C) Adam Faith D) Billy Fury

9) Which sign of the zodiac did Lester win on at 1-5 at Nottingham on 15 July 1971?

    A) Aries B) Leo C) Gemini D) Pisces

10) Which figure from the 'Wild West' did Lester win four times on in 1981?

    A) Custer B) Billy the Kid C) Kit Carson D) The Sundance Kid

Quiz No. 84

POT LUCK

1) In the 1980s, four years in a row the winner's name in Kempton's King George VI Chase ended with the same word. What was that word?

2) Which classic this century has been won by a poet, a country and a cricketer?

3) Which surname has cropped up twice among Derby-winning jockeys since the war?

4) Who were the only two horses to beat Nijinsky, one in the Champion Stakes and the other in the Arc?

5) In what year in the 1970s did the first four English classic winners all start with an M?

6) Which King George VI Chase winner sounds optimistic concerning a fish but pessimistic in regard to a dog?

7) In the first five years after World War Two, which word appears five times among the winners of the Cheltenham Gold Cup and the Grand National?

8) Which are the only two surnames associated with jockeys who have ridden a post-war winner of both the Derby and the Cheltenham Gold Cup?

9) Which was the last horse to win the Grand National with a number in its name?

10) Which horse completed a trio of wins at Ascot in 2019 when it was successful in the Victoria Cup, the Wokingham and the Bengough Stakes?

Quiz No. 85

QUOTES

1) 'Police could not prevent women from rushing the cordon and picking hairs out of his tail for mementos.' Which trainer on which horse?

   A) Basil Briscoe on Golden Miller B) Tom Dreaper on Arkle
   C) David Elsworth on Desert Orchid D) Henrietta Knight on Best Mate

2) 'My favourite horse was Never Say Die. It was a great Derby when we first saw the genius of Lester Piggott, and I'll never forget that race or horse.' Which Rolling Stone?

   A) Mick Jagger B) Keith Richards C) Charlie Watts D) Ronnie Wood

3) 'Hopefully, they will leave those bastards in the bowler hats in place when they commence the demolition.' Which Dave on Ascot's redevelopment in 2005?

   A) Dave Ashforth B) Dave Cleary C) Dave Nevison D) Dave Yates

4) 'You can't run the horse at Salisbury, the lunch there is terrible.' Which member of the upper class has more things on her mind than racing?

   A) Lady Beaverbrook B) Lady Halifax C) Lady Sassoon
   D) The Duchess of Norfolk

5) 'The great joy of jump racing is that everyone with whom you rub shoulders in the stands in a bitter November rain is a true believer.' Which Labour politician in 2004?

   A) Tony Blair B) Gordon Brown C) Robin Cook D) John Prescott

6) 'Having a dance band on a racecourse is a bit like having a snooker table on a boat.' Which trainer?

   A) Richard Hannon Senior B) Richard Hannon Junior
   C) John Gosden D) David Elsworth

7) 'I don't follow particular horses, although the horses I back seem to.' Which football manager rues his luck?

A) Terry Venables B) Tommy Docherty C) Alex Ferguson
D) Harry Redknapp

8) 'It has always been a mystery to me why our best race should be run on our worst racecourse.' Which media pundit doesn't much care for Epsom?

A) Julian Wilson B) Matt Chapman C) Alastair Down
D) John McCririck

9) 'Yes sir, I've got two actually. The first is that I'm bored with this film and could you please put something different on and, secondly, when will the usherette be bringing the ice creams and popcorn?' Which jockey when asked by a senior steward at Worcester after seeing several re-runs of a race, if he had any more comments to make?

A) Terry Biddlecombe B) John Francome C) Tony McCoy
D) Jonjo O'Neill

10) 'A good jockey doesn't need orders and a bad one forgets them.' Which jumps trainer?

A) Nicky Henderson B) Paul Nicholls C) Willie Mullins
D) Jonjo O'Neill

Quiz No. 86

SECONDS, ANYONE?

1) How frustrated his connections must have been that he was foaled in the same year as the mighty Frankel. He was runner-up to him in five races in 2011 and 2012 when trained by both Marco Botti and Aidan O'Brien. Who was he?

2) In 1969 a horse ridden by Brian Taylor finished second in the Derby and then, nine years later, a jockey with the same name as that horse also finished second in the Derby. What name is involved here?

3) Which horse trained by Mick Channon was runner-up in the Arc three years running in 2007, 2008 and 2009?

4) Which horse trained by Martin Pipe came second three times in a row in the Long Walk Hurdle at Ascot in 1998, 1999 and 2000 before finally winning it in 2002?

5) In the last 25 years to 2021, which two horses have been runners-up in the Champion Hurdle on three occasions each?

6) This colt finished second in so many races, including the 2,000 Guineas and Derby of 1856, that his name was used for several years on the turf to label a horse that had a propensity to always find one too good for it. Who was he?

   A) Blue Barry B) Green Gawain C) Red Ronnie D) Yellow Jack

7) Which county, owned by Khalid Abdulla and trained by Andre Fabre, was second in the Arc in both 2014 and 2015?

8) From his name it sounds as though this Richard Fahey-trained horse might have been expressing his annoyance at finishing second in the Ayr Gold Cup in both 2016 and 2019. Who was he?

9) Fran Berry and this horse were second in the Wokingham at Royal Ascot in 2011 and 2012, but the horse did go on about it a bit too much! What was it called?

10) Trainer Barry Hills was unlucky to finish in second place in the Chester Cup two years running in 2010 and 2011, particularly on the first occasion when Richard Hills almost compensated for a terrible draw with a great ride, narrowly going down to Mamlook. What was the horse called?

Quiz No. 87

SEQUENCES

Here, in order, are four winners of big races. Can you complete the sequence with the next winner in each instance?

1) Camelot, Ruler of the World, Australia, Golden Horn, -----

2) Sayyedati, Las Meninas, Harayir, Bosra Sham, -----

3) Punjabi, Binocular, Hurricane Fly, Rock on Ruby, -----

4) Tirol, Mystiko, Rodrigo De Triano, Zafonic, -----

5) Alexandrova, Light Shift, Look Here, Sariska, -----

6) War of Attrition, Kauto Star, Denman, Kauto Star, -----

7) Harbour Law, Capri, Kew Gardens, Logician, -----

8) Enable, Poet's Word, Enable, Enable, -----

9) Special Tiara, Altior, Altior, Politologue, -----

10) Rail Link, Dylan Thomas, Zarkava, Sea the Stars, -----

Quiz No. 88

'SORRY MATE, IT'S NOT HERE THIS YEAR!'

On occasion, for a variety of reasons, races that are normally associated with a particular racecourse are temporarily moved elsewhere. Here are a list of races and dates. Can you match them up with the courses at the foot of the page to indicate where they were held on those dates?

1) The Haydock Sprint Cup of 2008

2) The Doncaster St Leger of 2006

3) Ascot's King George of 2005

4) Doncaster's November Handicap of 2006

5) The Epsom Derby between 1915 and 1918

6) Newmarket's Cambridgeshire of 1940

7) Kempton's King George VI Chase of 1995

8) Doncaster's Lincoln Handicap between 1942 and 1945

9) Aintree's Grand National between 1916 and 1918

10) Doncaster's St Leger of 1940

Substitute Courses

Doncaster, Gatwick, Newbury, Newmarket, Nottingham, Pontefract, Sandown, Thirsk, Windsor, York

Quiz No. 89

TOP JUMPS RACES –
A SELECTION – No. 1 THE CHARLIE HALL
VENUE – Wetherby DISTANCE – 3m FIRST RUN – 1969

1) Six horses have won the Charlie Hall Chase twice. They include two that begin with the letter O. One of them was successful in 1996 and 1997 while the other won the race in 2005 and 2007. Who were the two horses?

2) The 2009 winner shared its name with a rock group and was trained by Evan Williams and ridden by Paul Moloney. What was it called?

   A) Black Sabbath B) Deep Purple C) Jethro Tull D) Steely Dan

3) Wayward Lad was the first horse to win the Charlie Hall on more than one occasion, doing so in 1983 and 1985. Unusually, two trainers and two jockeys were involved in his success. Who were the four people?

4) Since 1990 only one man has trained the winner of the Charlie Hall six times. Who is it?

   A) Howard Johnson B) Paul Nicholls C) David Pipe
   D) Nigel Twiston-Davies

5) Who are the only two jockeys this century to win back-to-back Charlie Hall Chases, one doing so in 2003 and 2004 and the other in 2008 and 2009?

6) The only time the race has ended in a dead-heat was in 1976 when Current Gold couldn't be separated from a horse with a name pertaining to tennis. Who was it?

   A) Deuce B) Love Thirty C) Second Serve D) Set Point

7) The only two female-trained winners this century were Sackville in 2001 and Irish Cavalier in 2016. Which two women trained them?

8) Of the four horses that have won both the Charlie Hall and the Cheltenham Gold Cup, which two, one in the 1970s and the other in the 1980s, shared the same last word of their names?

9) In a second link with tennis, the 1977 winner was a winner of the women's title at Wimbledon. What was it called?

A) Brough B) Bueno C) Evert D) Goolagong

10) The 2012 Charlie Hall winner went on to take two King Georges at Kempton, while the 2015 winner was also successful at that event in the same year that he won the Charlie Hall. Who were the two horses?

Quiz No. 90

TOP JUMPS RACES – A SELECTION – No. 2 THE FIGHTING FIFTH HURDLE

VENUE – Newcastle DISTANCE – Two miles, half furlong FIRST RUN – 1969

1) Already a big deal, this race attained Grade One status in 2004. Which legendary horse won the race three times in a row in 1972, 1973 and 1974, a feat that no horse has repeated?

2) Only one other horse has won the Fighting Fifth three times. It did so in 1976, 1977 and 1979, and would have won an unprecedented four times but for disqualification in 1980. Which horse, trained by Bob Turnell, is being described here?

3) For the first time in the history of the race a dead-heat was called in 2021 between which two horses?

4) Which horse trained by Malcolm Jefferson and ridden by Lorcan Wyer was the only back-to-back winner of the 1990s when it took the prize in 1998 and 1999?

5) Mercy Rimell became the first woman to train the winner of the Fighting Fifth with Gaye Brief in 1983, but in the following year it happened again when Browne's Gazette took the race. Which woman trained it?

6) Two more female trainers were successful in the 1990s: the first with Batabanoo in 1994 and the second with Space Trucker in 1996. Who were they?

7) Up to 2021 only one horse trained by Paul Nicholls has been successful in the race, winning it in 2014 and 2016. What was it called?

8) Which Nicky Richards-trained horse won the Fighting Fifth in 2003, but also finished second twice and third twice in the event?

9) Noel Meade trained the winner in the 2009 running when Go Native prevailed, but he had earlier won it in 2004 and 2007 with a ridiculously talented animal that didn't quite see the point in going flat out to get to a pole in the ground in front of another horse, and would have said so if only he could speak! Who was he?

10) Which trainer saddled Floyd, who was the only horse to win back-to-back races in the 1980s when successful in 1987 and 1988?

A) Mick Easterby B) David Elsworth C) Reg Hollinshead
D) Martin Pipe

Quiz No. 91

TOP JUMPS RACES – A SELECTION –
No. 3 THE HENNESSY
(NOW THE LADBROKES TROPHY)
VENUE – Newbury DISTANCE – 3m 1f 214y FIRST RUN – 1957

1) The first two runnings were not at Newbury. On which course were they run?

   A) Aintree B) Cheltenham C) Haydock Park D) Sandown Park

2) Trevor Hemmings was a great supporter of jumps racing over many years and he won the last race before his death in 2020 and the first race after his death in 2021 with which two horses, the first trained by Jonjo O'Neill and the last by Venetia Williams?

3) Which much-loved horse is the only one to win the race in two different decades, and also the only one to win it on two different courses?

4) Up to 2021 nine horses have won the Hennessy and the Cheltenham Gold Cup. Three of them began with B. They won the Newbury race in 1982, 1984 and 2012. Who were they?

5) The last horse, up to 2021, to win both the Hennessy and the Gold Cup, took the former in 2016 in the last year of their record-breaking sponsorship before it became the Ladbrokes Trophy. Who was he?

6) Bob and Andy Turnell teamed up to produce the only winner of the Hennessy that doubled as a date when they took the 1975 running. What was it called?

7) Who is the only horse to win both the Hennessy and the Grand National?

8) Which horse, ridden by John Cook and trained by Edward Courage, won the 1969 Hennessy before going on to be placed in three successive Grand Nationals in the 1970s?

9) Colin Tizzard trained two horses that finished second in the race in 2015 and 2021 and you may have consulted the first one in order to

go and see the second one! What were the names of the two horses?

10) Emma Lavelle and Ben Jones combined in producing the winner of the 2019 event. It sounds like the area of the supermarket you might go to purchase bacon. What was it called?

Quiz No. 92

TOP JUMPS RACES – A SELECTION – No. 4 THE IMPERIAL CUP

VENUE – Sandown Park DISTANCE – 2m FIRST RUN – 1907

1) It's something of a surprise that it's been allowed to keep its title in the woke madness we are currently living through! A Fulke Walwyn-trained horse whose name suggests spying and subterfuge is the only horse since the war to win the Imperial Cup in different decades when successful in 1949 and 1950. What was it called?

2) Which popular holiday destination won the race in 1973 before going on to win the Champion Hurdle the following year, trained by Fred Winter and ridden by Richard Pitman?

3) The Skeltons combined to take the 2021 running of the race with a combination of a karate expert and a dual winner of the Masters golf major. What was its name?

4) It certainly was a Magic Combination when that horse took the spoils in 2000 for jockey David Casey and which trainer?

5) Olympian in 1993, Blowing Wind in 1998 and Gaspara in 2007 had something else in common besides being trained by the Pipes. What was it?

6) Flaming East in 1958, Desert Hero in 1983 and Scorned in 2004 were the oldest winners of the Imperial Cup at what age?

A) Eight B) Nine C) Ten D) Eleven

7) Which two jockeys have won the Imperial Cup for both Martin and David Pipe?

8) What is the link between Ibal, who won the race in 2001, Alarazi, who was successful in 2011, and First Avenue, who took the prize in 2013?

9) Peter Scudamore has won the Imperial Cup on a horse trained by Martin Pipe, while his son Tom has ridden the winner of the race for Martin's son David. True or false?

10) Which island won the 1948 edition of the Imperial Cup for trainer Staff Ingham?

A) Anglesey B) Canvey Island C) Lindisfarne D) Skye

Quiz No. 93

TOP JUMPS RACES – A SELECTION – No. 5 THE IRISH GRAND NATIONAL

VENUE – Fairyhouse DISTANCE – 3m 5f FIRST RUN – 1870

1) The first winner of the Irish Grand National was a Prime Minister in the shape of Sir Robert Peel, and in 1876 it was won by a horse actually called Grand National! Which TV sit-com was successful in 1898?

A) Cheers B) The Good Life C) Outnumbered D) Porridge

2) Which surname trained the winner of the race 13 times between 1949 and 1978?

3) It was an all-female affair in 2015 when Katie Walsh won on a horse trained by Sandra Hughes. What was it called?

4) Two horses that both humped 12 stone round Fairyhouse to win it, one in 1964 and the other in 1990, were also the only two winners of the race to also have a Cheltenham Gold Cup win on their CV. Who were they?

5) Which horse would have added his name to the two above if, after winning at Fairyhouse in 1979, he had not been disqualified at Cheltenham in the 1980 Gold Cup?

6) Which 2011 winner of the race for trainer Arthur Moore and jockey Nina Carberry could perhaps provide a description of most countries' governmental approach to the pandemic?

7) Five years later when Rogue Angel won the race both owner and trainer had a link to animals. Who were they?

8) When Feathered Gala prevailed in 1996 the second was an earlier Cheltenham Gold Cup winner, and the third was a later Cheltenham Gold Cup winner. Who were they?

9) Which Neil Young album was runner-up in the Irish Grand National in 1993 and 1995?

A) Harvest B) On The Beach C) Rust never Sleeps D) Zuma

10) Four horses have won the Irish National and the English National. Rhyme N'Reason, Bobbyjo and Numbersixvalverde have been the most recent, but the first of them was Ascetics Silver who won the Irish version in 1904 and the English one in 1906. What was unusual about his Aintree win?

Quiz No. 94

TOP JUMPS RACES – A SELECTION – No. 6 THE LONG WALK HURDLE

VENUE – Ascot DISTANCE – 3m 97y FIRST RUN – 1965

1) Big Buck's and Reve De Sivola dominated the race for six years, winning it three times each between 2009 and 2014. Nicky Henderson's first winner of the race in 2008 was the last before that pair took over things, and a Colin Tizzard-trained horse stopped their run when he beat Reve De Sivola in 2015. Who were the two horses who bookended that great pairs' achievement?

2) Who is the only jockey to have won The Long Walk Hurdle in two centuries?

    A) Thierry Doumen B) Richard Johnson C) Tony McCoy
    D) Ruby Walsh

3) Up to 2021 which horse has been the latest to gain two wins in the race when he won both the 2018 and 2020 runnings with Aidan Coleman and Emma Lavelle involved as well?

4) The 1978 Long Walk winner was trained by Jumbo Wilkinson and ridden by Steve Charlton, and its name referenced a northern jumps track. What was it called?

5) Up to 2021 six horses have gone on from winning The Long Walk Hurdle in December to land the World Hurdle at Cheltenham the following March. The first to do so was Derring Rose who won the Ascot event in 1980. The jockey and trainer could hardly be more respected. Who were they?

6) Which horse who proved himself rather useful on the flat by winning the Cesarewitch, the Chester Cup, the Newbury Autumn Cup and the Queen Alexandra Stakes, also won, for jockey Steve Smith-Eccles and trainer Harry Thomson-Jones, two Long Walks in 1977 and 1979?

7) The 1989 winner of the race was unique in going on to win the Grand National for trainer Jenny Pitman later in his career. Who was he?

8) Unique in another way was the 1975 victor under John Francome who was going up in trip after success in the previous year's Champion Hurdle at Cheltenham. Who was he?

9) Thierry Doumen rode the brilliant four-time winner Baracouda in his first three successes in the race, but who was on board when he won for the final time in 2004, and where was the race run?

10) Out of the Gloom in 1986 and Bluff Cove in 1987 were successive winners of The Long Walk Hurdle. They were ridden by Peter Scudamore and Richard Dunwoody, but which man trained them both?

Quiz No. 95

TOP JUMPS RACES – A SELECTION –
No. 7 THE SCOTTISH GRAND NATIONAL
VENUE – Ayr DISTANCE – 4m FIRST RUN – 1867

1) The race has been run at Ayr since 1966, with Brasher's 1965 victory coming in the last running of the race at which defunct track?

2) Who is the only horse to have won the Scottish and English Grand National in the same year?

3) Ruby Walsh had just one win in the Scottish National and it came on which Martin Pipe-trained horse in 2002?

4) Which male first name appeared in both the 2005 winner and the 2018 winner of the race?

5) Merigo, trained by Andrew Parker and ridden by Timmy Murphy, won the race in 2010, came second in 2011, and won it again in 2012. In that latter success the horse that finished second went on to win at Aintree in the following year's Grand National. Who was it?

6) The 2000 winner, ridden by Adrian Maguire and trained by Ferdy Murphy, is composed of a capital city and a fish. What was it called?

7) The youngest winner of the race since the war landed it in 1994 and was six years old when it did so. The following year Willsford became, at 12 years of age, the oldest winner since the war. The six-year-old went on to even greater glory in the Grand National at Aintree later in his career. Who was he?

8) Which horse who won the race in successive years for Paul Nicholls and Sam Twiston-Davies in 2016 and 2017 experienced a change of ownership between the two races?

9) Which horse trained by Philip Hobbs finished third behind Young Kenny in the 1999 event and may well have reduced the 15-lengths margin if it hadn't overindulged at breakfast?

10) The 2015 winner, trained by Hilary Parrott and ridden by Robbie Dunne, could well have had a royal personage in mind! What was it called?

Quiz No. 96

TOP JUMPS RACES – A SELECTION –
No. 8 THE TRIUMPH HURDLE
VENUE – Cheltenham DISTANCE – 2m 1f FIRST RUN – 1939

1) Who is the only horse to win the Triumph Hurdle and go on to win the Grand National?

2) Who are the only two horses that begin with the same letter to win both the Triumph Hurdle and the Champion Hurdle; the first of them landing the big one in 1990 and the second in 2008?

3) Who is the only man to train the winner of the Triumph Hurdle in four different decades?

4) Six of the first seven winners of the race were French, but since 1955 they have experienced a drought. The exception came in 2000 when father and son Francois and Thierry Doumen scored with which horse?

5) Robert Thornton and Alan King combined to win the Triumph Hurdle in 2005 with which town in Cornwall?

   A) Falmouth B) Penzance C) St. Austell D) St. Ives

6) Which winner of the Triumph Hurdle went on to take three Champion Hurdles in succession?

7) Which flat jockey won the race on Prince Charlemagne in 1954?

   A) Scobie Breasley B) Joe Mercer C) Lester Piggott D) Doug Smith

8) Rachael Blackmore became the first female jockey to taste success in the Triumph Hurdle in 2021 on which horse?

9) Who is the only jockey to ride the winner of the Triumph hurdle five times this century?

10) Trainer John Quinn teamed up with jockey Dougie Costello the only time either of them won the Triumph Hurdle with which 33-1 shot in 2012?

Quiz No. 97

TOP JUMPS RACES – A SELECTION –
No. 9 THE WELSH GRAND NATIONAL
VENUE – Chepstow DISTANCE – 3m 6½f FIRST RUN – 1895

1) Which horse who won the Welsh National in 2013 and 2015 was in the rare situation of having a new owner, trainer and jockey when he won it the second time?

2) Three people with the same surname have trained the winner of the Welsh National this century. Who are they?

3) Which Paul Nicholls-trained horse has been a model of consistency in finishing third in the race in 2018, 2019 and 2020?

4) Which horse trained by Alan King won the race in 2006, finished second in 2007, and third in 2008?

5) Which trainer monopolised the event between 1988 and 1993, winning five of the six contests?

6) Who was the only jockey to win the Welsh National in this century and the previous one?

7) The winners of the race in successive years in 2003 and 2004 were Bindaree and Silver Birch. Bindaree had already won the Aintree equivalent and Silver Birch went on to do so. Jim Culloty and Robbie Power were the riders in Liverpool but which two jockeys enjoyed success at Chepstow?

8) The 1983 winner of the race went on to take the Cheltenham Gold Cup the following year, and the 1990 winner took one year longer before he landed the big one. Who were the two horses?

9) In this century, up to 2021, it has happened another two times. The 2010 winner triumphed at Cheltenham in 2012, and the 2016 winner brought home the Gold Cup in 2018. Which two horses were involved?

10) Fred Rimell, Jenny Pitman and Nigel Twiston-Davies have all trained horses in the 1970s, 1980s and 1990s respectively that have completed the Grand National double by winning at both Chepstow and Aintree, although only one did so in the same season. Which three horses were responsible?

Quiz No. 98

TOP JUMPS RACES – A SELECTION –
No. 10 THE WHITBREAD GOLD CUP
VENUE – Sandown Park DISTANCE – 3m 5f FIRST RUN – 1957

1) Since its long-running sponsorship by the Whitbread Company it has had three more in this century, and is now called the bet365 Gold Cup, but to me it will always be the Whitbread. Since 1957 only one horse has won the race going off at odds on. Who was it?

2) Which trainer won the race in 1989 with Brown Windsor and then had to wait a quarter of a century before winning it again with Hadrian's Approach in 2014?

3) Which horse trained by Fulke Walwyn and ridden by Bill Smith is the only one to win the race in two different decades, taking the prize in 1979 and 1981?

4) Jockey Ron Barry won the Whitbread in 1971 on Titus Oates, and then, in 1973 on Charlie Potheen, became the only man to win the race at two different courses because the 1973 event took place at a different venue. Which track was it on?

   A) Ascot B) Cheltenham C) Kempton Park D) Newcastle

5) Ruby Walsh won the race twice on the same horse. The first time was in 2001, the last year of Whitbread's sponsorship, and the second was in 2003. The horse, trained by Paul Nicholls, would probably have won a Grand National if he hadn't been brought down when going well at Aintree in 2002. Who was he?

6) The 2020 running was another victim of Covid, but which trainer landed the spoils either side of that year with Talkischeap and Potterman?

7) Which horse trained by Fulke Walwyn stuffed his rivals at 100-6 in the 1958 Whitbread?

8) Which horse was allowed to go off at 25-1 for the first bet365 Gold Cup Chase of 2008, ending up in the winners' enclosure alongside Richard Johnson, Philip Hobbs and Mr. M.G. St. Quinton?

9) Henllan Harri became the biggest-priced winner of the race when doing the business for Peter and Sean Bowen in 2017. What price did it win at?

A) 33-1 B) 40-1 C) 50-1 D) 66-1

10) Who trained the first winner of the race in 1957 when Much Obliged prevailed, and went on to be the first man to train back-to-back winners of the race with Hoodwinked in 1963 and Dormant in 1964?

A) Neville Crump B) Ryan Price C) Bob Turnell D) Fulke Walwyn

Quiz No. 99

WHAT WERE THE ODDS ON THAT?

1) By what unusual price did Kribensis, trained by Michael Stoute and ridden by Richard Dunwoody, win the Champion Hurdle at Cheltenham in 1990?

   A) 75-40 B) 13-5 C) 95-40 D) 14-5

2) What price was Nijinsky returned at when he won Ascot's King George in 1970?

3) The Stewards' Cup winner in 2010, trained by Dandy Nicholls and ridden by Billy Cray, had a name that referenced prices. What was it?

4) In 2011, 2012 and 2013 the Oaks at Epsom was won by Dancing Rain, Was and Talent in that order. They all started at the same price. What was it?

   A) 10-1 B) 12-1 C) 16-1 D) 20-1

5) The same thing happened in Cheltenham's Queen Mother Champion Chase in 1998, 1999 and 2000. The horses were One Man, Call Equiname and Edredon Bleu respectively. They all started at which price?

   A) 5-2 B) 7-2 C) 9-2 D) 11-2

6) Who are the three colts that have won the Derby at odds-on since the war?

7) Never Say Die in 1954, Ribero in 1968 and Classic Cliché in 1995 are the only three colts to win the St Leger at this price since the war. What price?

8) An actual price won Royal Ascot's Queens Vase in 1958, trained by Vincent O'Brien and ridden by Scobie Breasley. What was it called?

   A) Double Carpet B) Burlington Bertie C) Even Money
   D) Four to Six

9) How many years in a row this century has the King George at Ascot been won by the favourite?

10) In Desert Orchid's four wins in Kempton's King George VI Chase between 1986 and 1990 what was the longest and shortest price he was returned at?

Quiz No. 100

WILD CARD

1) Which is the only surname this century that has appeared in the winners of both the flat jockeys' title and the jump jockeys' title?

2) Who won the 2,000 Guineas 52 years after his death?

3) Which city has won the Arc, the Cesarewitch and the Triumph Hurdle?

4) Which two fathers and sons trained a winner of the Derby in the second half of the 20th century?

5) The last time the horse and jockey's surname of a Grand National winner started with the same letter was in the 1969 running of the race. Who were that horse and jockey?

6) Which post-war winner of the Champion Hurdle is the only one to have a football club in its name?

7) The 1932 Derby produced the only occasion when the race was won by a date. What date was it?

8) Which surname has trained the winner of the four-and-a-quarter-mile Grand National and the six-furlong July Cup this century?

9) The last time the winner of the Arc had a number in its name was in 1979. What was the horse called?

10) A man who won the Grand National as a jockey and a trainer in the last century has had his surname used for an English Classic-winning horse of this century. What is that name?

ANSWERS

Quiz No. 1 – ALPHABET ALLEY – A

1) Aldaniti, Amberleigh House and Auroras Encore
2) Azertyuiop
3) Animal Kingdom, African Story and Arrogate
4) Attivo
5) At Fisher's Cross
6) Arctic Cosmos
7) Alycidon
8) Alberta's Run
9) Altesse Royale
10) Anthony Van Dyck and Anapurna

Quiz No. 2 – ALPHABET ALLEY – B

1) Boucher, Bustino and Bruni
2) Bonanza Boy
3) Bishops Court
4) Buena Vista
5) Binocular
6) Bertie's Dream, Bobs Worth and Brindisi Breeze
7) Bostons Angel
8) Brown Windsor
9) Banks Hill
10) Big Zeb

Quiz No. 3 – ALPHABET ALLEY – C

1) Captain Steve
2) Carruthers
3) Curry
4) Cause of Causes
5) Choir Boy
6) Cool Ground and Cool Dawn
7) Cutting Blade
8) Church Island
9) Cut Above and Commanche Run
10) Caribbean Coral

Quiz No. 4 – ALPHABET ALLEY – D

1) Dynaste
2) Dylan Thomas and Duke of Marmalade
3) Dancing Brave, Don't Forget Me and Doyoun
4) Don Cossack
5) Double Cream
6) Dunguib
7) Dawn Approach
8) Douvan
9) Declaration of War
10) Drinny's Double

Quiz No. 5 – ALPHABET ALLEY – E

1) Entrepreneur
2) Eswarah
3) Encke
4) Erhaab
5) Eric
6) Elopement
7) Enable
8) Empery
9) Embassy
10) Edredon Bleu

Quiz No. 6 – ALPHABET ALLEY – F

1) Flying Diplomat
2) Fairway
3) Frodon
4) First Bout
5) Faugheen
6) Foxtrot
7) Found
8) Freebooter
9) Footpad
10) Forever Together

Quiz No. 7 – ALPHABET ALLEY – G

1) Grittar
2) Ghanaati
3) Golden Horn
4) Golan
5) Garrison Savannah
6) Ginevra
7) Gloomy Sunday
8) Golden Fleece
9) Go Native
10) Generous

Quiz No. 8 – ALPHABET ALLEY – H

1) Helvellyn
2) High Top
3) Haafhd and Henrythenavigator
4) Harbinger
5) Hatoof and Harayir
6) Horseradish
7) Hurricane Run
8) Holding Court
9) Halling
10) Hogmaneigh and Holbeck Ghyll

Quiz No. 9 – ALPHABET ALLEY – I

1) Ile de Bourbon
2) Island Sands
3) Immortal Verse
4) Identity Thief
5) Ivanovich Gorbatov
6) Intermission
7) Imperial Call
8) I Cried For You
9) Idaho
10) In The Wings

Quiz No. 10 – ALPHABET ALLEY – J

1) Jodami
2) Jack High
3) Juventus
4) Jay Trump
5) Julio Mariner
6) Junior
7) Joey Jones
8) Jupiter Island
9) Jimmy Styles, Jimmy Reppin and Jimmy The Singer
10) Josies Orders

Quiz No. 11 – ALPHABET ALLEY – K

1) Kilmarnock
2) Kalaglow
3) Kilburn
4) Kayudee
5) Kris Kin
6) Ki Ming
7) King's Ride and King's Glory
8) Kahyasi
9) Kayf Aramis
10) Kamundu

Quiz No. 12 – ALPHABET ALLEY – L

1) Lake Coniston
2) Limini, Let's Dance and Laurina
3) Longboat
4) Low Sun
5) Linden Tree
6) Las Vegas
7) Lammtarra
8) Last Suspect and Little Polveir
9) Le Havre
10) Lillie Langtry

Quiz No. 13 – ALPHABET ALLEY – M

1) Magic Flute
2) Martial
3) Mecca's Angel
4) Morecambe
5) Missed Approach
6) Montjeu
7) Moon Racer
8) Mill House
9) Mtoto
10) Mr. What and Mr. Frisk

Quiz No. 14 – ALPHABET ALLEY – N

1) Nedawi
2) Newcastle
3) Nupsala
4) North Star
5) Nougat
6) Nijinsky, Nonoalco and Nebbiolo
7) Ninetieth Minute
8) Not Out
9) Noble Prince
10) Novellist

Quiz No. 15 – ALPHABET ALLEY – O

1) One In A Million and On The House
2) Our Conor
3) Observatory
4) On The Fringe
5) Old Bill
6) Olympic Glory
7) Oh So Sharp
8) Opera House
9) Owington
10) Oiseau De Nuit

Quiz No. 16 – ALPHABET ALLEY – P

1) Pentland Hills
2) Pilsudski
3) Pendil
4) Predominate
5) Proverb
6) Puntal, Poker De Sivola and Potterman
7) Petong
8) Panorama
9) Psidium
10) Persian Punch

Quiz No. 17 – ALPHABET ALLEY – Q

1) Quizair
2) Quest For Fame
3) Quare Times
4) Qualify
5) Quashed
6) Quentin Collonges
7) Quick Reply
8) Qualando
9) Quorum
10) Queen Of Trumps

Quiz No. 18 – ALPHABET ALLEY – R

1) Relko
2) Royal Oath
3) Roksana
4) Rostropovich
5) Ribocco and Ribero
6) Refuse To Bend
7) Rakti
8) Riverside Theatre
9) Rail Link
10) Rip Van Winkle

Quiz No. 19 – ALPHABET ALLEY – S

1) Spring Heeled
2) Salsify
3) Suamarez, Suave Dancer and Subotica
4) Stumps
5) Shergar
6) Summoner
7) Showboat
8) Sergeant Cecil
9) Salsabil
10) Southern Power

Quiz No. 20 – ALPHABET ALLEY – T

1) To The Roof
2) Ten Sovereigns
3) Time Machine
4) Trempolino and Tonybin
5) Thunder Snow
6) Trabolgan
7) Time Charter
8) Tumbledownwind
9) Tea For Three
10) Telescope

Quiz No. 21 – ALPHABET ALLEY – U

1) US Navy Flag
2) User Friendly
3) Ushers Island
4) Umbria
5) Une Artiste
6) Urban Sea
7) Umpire
8) Uxizandre
9) Unfuwain
10) Un Temps Pour Tout

Quiz No. 22 – ALPHABET ALLEY – V

1) Vroum Vroum Mag
2) Vimy
3) Virginia Boy
4) Voltaire
5) Vautour
6) Vinnie Row
7) Vitiges
8) Vision D'Etat
9) Veracity
10) Voy Por Ustedes

Quiz No. 23 – ALPHABET ALLEY – W

1) Whip It Quick
2) Wolver Hollow
3) Waterloo Bridge
4) Winker Watson
5) What's Up Boys
6) Warrsan
7) Warning
8) Western Dancer
9) West Tip
10) Weapons Amnesty

Quiz No. 24 – ALPHABET ALLEY – X

1) Xandover
2) Xerxes
3) Xanthus
4) Xenophon
5) Xeny
6) Xaar
7) X-Rated
8) Xanadu
9) Xtrasensory
10) Xebee

Quiz No. 25 – ALPHABET ALLEY – Y

1) Yoyo
2) Youth
3) Young Eclipse
4) Yorkhill
5) Yorkshire Blue
6) Yeast
7) Yellow River
8) Yaroslav
9) Yorick
10) Young Emperor

Quiz No. 26 – ALPHABET ALLEY – Z
1) Zonda
2) Zodiac
3) Zorba
4) Zuider Zee
5) Zeta's Son
6) Zino and Zafonic
7) Zarathustra
8) Zucchero
9) Zoffany
10) Zarib, Zaynar and Zarkandar

Quiz No. 27 – ANYTHING GOES
1) Carl Llewellyn
2) They all beat Red Rum
3) Ginger McCain and Nigel Twiston-Davies
4) Jamie Osborne
5) Bird of Fortune
6) Diamond Harry, Restless Harry and Unowhatimeanharry
7) He won the Irish Derby and the Irish National and with horses from the same mare
8) Love Divine and Love
9) Whiteoak and Black Tears
10) Thierry Jarnet

Quiz No. 28 – CHASING DREAMS AT THE CHELTENHAM FESTIVAL
1) Alan King, Nicky Henderson and Willie Mullins, who has done so twice
2) Wichita Lineman, Alfie Sherrin and Holywell
3) Denman, Bobs Worth and Lord Windermere
4) Garde Champetre and Balthazar King
5) Black Hercules
6) Min
7) Milan Native
8) Sheila Crow, Ian Ferguson, Rodger Sweeney and Liam Lennon
9) B -Ferdy Murphy with L'Antartique and Divers
10) Edredon Bleu

Quiz No. 29 – CLASSIC CONUMDRUMS
1) A – Aida
2) B – Noel Murless
3) D – Lester Piggott
4) D – Rockavon
5) A – Ralph Beckett
6) A – Augusta
7) B - Jack Charlton
8) B – Joseph O'Brien
9) C – Dick Hern
10) C – Ryan Moore

Quiz No. 30 – CRYPTIC CLASSIC-WINNING JOCKEYS
1) Michael Hills
2) Freddy Head
3) Brian Rouse
4) Neville Sellwood
5) Eddie Hide
6) Kerrin McEvoy
7) Seamie Heffernan
8) Jimmy Fortune
9) Greville Starkey
10) Geoff Lewis

Quiz No. 31 – CRYPTIC GRAND NATIONAL-WINNING JOCKEYS – PART 1

1) Richard Guest
2) Steve Knight
3) Aubrey Hastings
4) Eddie Dempsey
5) Jimmy Frost
6) Tim Norman
7) Ryan Mania
8) Bob Champion
9) Tommy Carberry
10) John Burke

Quiz No. 32 – CRYPTIC GRAND NATIONAL-WINNING JOCKEYS – PART 2

1) Charlie Fenwick
2) Frank Furlong
3) Dave Dick
4) John Buckingham
5) Maurice Barnes
6) John Cook
7) Graham Lee
8) Fred Winter
9) Tim Hyde
10) Henry Coventry

Quiz No. 33 – THE DEFINITE ARTICLE

1) The Minstrel
2) The Bug
3) The Dice Man
4) The Shah
5) The Hertford
6) The Spaniard
7) The Plumber's Mate
8) The Solent
9) The Dikler
10) The Last Lion

Quiz No. 34 – THE DERBY

1) Authorized, Australia, Anthony Van Dyck and Adayar
2) Pinza
3) Roberto Firmino
4) Troy and Oath
5) A – Lapdog and Spaniel
6) B – The Flying Dutchman
7) Champion
8) Archduke
9) Ladas
10) Noble and Moses

Quiz No. 35 – FAVOURITE RACEHORSES ON THE FLAT No. 1 – BRIGADIER GERARD

1) Jean Hislop, Dick Hern and Joe Mercer
2) They are the only horses to twice finish second to Brigadier Gerard
3) Rheingold
4) Newbury
5) True
6) Riverman
7) Salisbury

8) The Middle Park Stakes
9) 11-2
10) The Champagne Stakes and the Champion Stakes at Salisbury and Newmarket

Quiz No. 36 – FAVOURITE RACEHORSES ON THE FLAT
No. 2 – DANCING BRAVE

1) Sandown Park
2) The Craven Stakes
3) Green Desert
4) The Aga Khan, Michael Stoute and Walter Swinburn
5) Starkey rode him six times to Eddery's four
6) Shardari finished second and Petoski finished fifth
7) Goodwood
8) Bering
9) The Breeders' Cup Turf at Santa Anita
10) Commander in Chief

Quiz No. 37 – FAVOURITE RACEHORSES ON THE FLAT
No. 3 – FRANKEL

1) Nathaniel
2) Soft
3) 7-4 and 1-20
4) Ascot, Newbury, York and Doncaster, which was the one he faced just two horses on
5) Farhh
6) Cirrus Des Aigles
7) The Sussex Stakes
8) Rock of Gibraltar
9) Dubawi Gold
10) Cracksman

Quiz No. 38 – FAVOURITE RACEHORSES ON THE FLAT
No. 4 – GIANTS CAUSEWAY

1) The Iron Horse
2) C – Brahms
3) The Gladness Stakes
4) Five
5) King's Best
6) Kalinisi
7) George Duffield in the Eclipse
8) Naas
9) Medician
10) Tiznow

Quiz No. 39 – FAVOURITE RACEHORSES ON THE FLAT
No. 5 – PERSIAN PUNCH

1) C – Windsor
2) Deauville
3) Newmarket
4) True
5) Martin Dwyer, Richard Quinn, Ray Cochrane and Richard Hughes
6) The Jockey Club Cup
7) The Henry II Stakes
8) The Goodwood Cup and The Lonsdale Stakes
9) Celeric
10) Jardines Lookout and Millenary

Quiz No. 40 – FAVOURITE RACEHORSES OVER THE JUMPS
No. 1 – ARKLE

1) Tom Dreaper, Anne, Duchess of Westminster and a Scottish mountain peak
2) Himself

3) Mark Hely-Hutchinson
4) Navan
5) Ascot, Sandown Park, Kempton Park, Cheltenham and Newbury. He was undefeated on the first two
6) 35
7) The Leopardstown Chase
8) Dormant
9) Gowran Park
10) Pas Seul

Quiz No. 41 – FAVOURITE RACEHORSES OVER THE JUMPS
No. 2 – DENMAN

1) The Tank
2) Kauto Star, Imperial Commander and Long Run
3) Christian Williams, Ruby Walsh, Sam Thomas and AP McCoy. The first of the four has the 100 per cent record and the last never won on him
4) Bangor, Leopardstown and Punchestown
5) Exeter and Wincanton
6) Nicanor
7) Arkle
8) The Aon Chase
9) Don't Push It
10) An irregular heartbeat

Quiz No. 42 – FAVOURITE RACEHORSES OVER THE JUMPS
No. 3 – DESERT ORCHID

1) He fell at Kempton Park both times
2) Colin Brown
3) The Irish Grand National at Fairyhouse
4) Huntingdon
5) Norton's Coin and Garrison Savannah
6) The Fellow
7) Wincanton
8) Kildimo
9) Yahoo
10) A – Delius

Quiz No. 43 – FAVOURITE RACEHORSES OVER THE JUMPS
No. 4 – KAUTO STAR

1) Maia Eria
2) Mick Fitzgerald
3) AP McCoy
4) A – Auteuil
5) Exotic Dancer
6) 36 lengths and Imperial Commander
7) Denman and Neptune Collonges
8) Long Run
9) True
10) Because he won the Stayers' Triple Crown of King George VI Chase, Cheltenham Gold Cup and Betfair Chase

Quiz No. 44 – FAVOURITE RACEHORSES OVER THE JUMPS
No. 5 – MOSCOW FLYER

1) 26
2) Jessie Harrington
3) Paddy Moloney
4) The Arkle Chase
5) B – Nijinsky
6) Aintree
7) A – Down Royal

8) Istabraq
9) (a) 2003 and 2005   (b) 2003 and 2004   (c) 2004 and 2005
10) Cork

Quiz No. 45 – THE GEOGRAPHY OF THE DERBY

1) Blakeney and Morston
2) C – Teddington
3) Serpentine
4) Orlando
5) D – Paris
6) B – Doncaster
7) A – Bloomsbury
8) C – Ayrshire
9) Andover
10) Windsor Lad

Quiz No. 46 – GREYS

1) Newmarket
2) Ebaziyan
3) Silver Patriarch
4) Nicolaus Silver
5) C – The Lamb
6) Rooster Booster
7) Neptune Collonges
8) Grey Abbey
9) Monet's Garden
10) One Man

Quiz No. 47 – GROUP ONES No. 1 – THE ASCOT GOLD CUP

1) A – Brighton
2) Kieren Fallon, Mick Kinane and Johnny Murtagh
3) Paean
4) A – Foxfire
5) Westerner
6) Each horse had a different jockey when he won the race for a second time
7) Kayf Tara
8) B – Henry Cecil
9) Ely and Elf
10) Ardross

Quiz No. 48 – GROUP ONES No. 2 – THE CHAMPION STAKES

1) C – Springfield
2) Pilsudski
3) Two of his three wins were dead-heats
4) Petite Etoile
5) George Duffield and Mark Prescott
6) Baldric
7) Twice Over
8) Cirrus des Aigles
9) Corine Barande-Barbe and Lady Jane Cecil
10) Tony Cruz

Quiz No. 49 – GROUP ONES No. 3 – THE ECLIPSE

1) D – 18
2) Sea The Stars and Golden Horn
3) Environment Friend
4) It was run at Kempton Park
5) A – John Gosden
6) B – Busted
7) Hawk Wing and Hawkbill

8) Darryll Holland
9) Caerleon
10) (a) Brigadier Gerard (b) Dickens; the horse was Dickens Hill (c) HG Wells; the horse was Sadler's Wells (d) Ulysses

Quiz No. 50 – GROUP ONES No. 4 – THE HAYDOCK SPRINT CUP

1) Be Friendly and Peter O'Sullevan
2) A – Fog
3) They are the only seven-year-olds to win the race
4) African Rose
5) Green God and Green Desert
6) Eric Alston and Tim Easterby
7) Dandy and Adrian Nicholls and Regal Parade
8) Tim Sprake
9) Bruce Raymond
10) John Hammond

Quiz No. 51 – GROUP ONES No. 5 – THE INTERNATIONAL

1) Braulio Baeza
2) Hawaiian Sound
3) Dahlia, Ezzoud and Halling
4) Terimon
5) D – Walter Swinburn
6) Australia and Japan
7) Steve Cauthen
8) Gianfranco and Frankie Dettori
9) Commanche Run and Rodrigo de Triano
10) Gary Stevens

Quiz No. 52 – GROUP ONES No. 6 – THE JULY CUP

1) He was the only runner and walked over
2) Won the race three years in a row
3) Marchand d'Or
4) David Simcock
5) Stravinsky and Mozart
6) Starman
7) Concerto
8) Thatch and Thatching
9) Agnes World
10) Fleeting Spirit

Quiz No. 53 – GROUP ONES No. 7 – THE KING GEORGE VI & QUEEN ELIZABETH STAKES

1) Noel Murless and Saeed bin Suroor
2) Alamshar and Azamour
3) Dartmouth and Aureole
4) Dahlia and Swain
5) Crystal Ocean
6) Towser Gosden
7) Nijinsky and Montjeu
8) Opera House and King's Theatre
9) Petoski
10) B – Dylan Thomas

Quiz No. 54 – GROUP ONES No. 8 – THE LOCKINGE

1) Pall Mall
2) Ron Hutchinson and Richard Hughes
3) Ribchester
4) Own and train the winner
5) Russian Rhythm, Frankel and Night of Thunder

6) Young Generation
7) Sparkler
8) Michael Stoute, Michael Jarvis and Michael Bell
9) Canford Cliffs and Palace Pier
10) True

Quiz No. 55 – GROUP ONES No. 9 – THE NUNTHORPE

1) Oasis Dream
2) Jimmy Quinn and John Best
3) Bahamian Pirate
4) He was the only winner of the race on two different tracks because the 2008 running was at Newmarket
5) Pat Eddery and Steve Cauthen
6) Sole Power
7) Handsome Sailor and La Cucaracha
8) Lochsong, Lochangel and the bonus is Lochnager
9) D – The Tatling
10) Charlie Hills

Quiz No. 56 – GROUP ONES No. 10 – THE QUEEN ELIZABETH II STAKES

1) Willie Carson
2) Markofdistinction and Mark of Esteem
3) Terry Mills
4) Dubai Millennium
5) Ramonti, Raven's Pass and Rip Van Winkle
6) It was called World Cup
7) True
8) Freddy Head
9) Olivier Peslier
10) Wally Swinburn rode the first one and his son Walter the second

Quiz No. 57 – GROUP ONES No. 11 – THE ST JAMES'S PALACE STAKES

1) Black Minnaloushe
2) Ascot
3) Rock of Gibraltar, Henrythenavigator, Frankel, Dawn Approach, Gleneagles, Galileo Gold and Poetic Flare
4) B – Gladstone
5) Guy Harwood, Barry Hills and Geoff Huffer
6) £106
7) Zafeen
8) Without Parole
9) Six
10) B – Goya

Quiz No. 58 – GROUP ONES No. 12 – THE SUSSEX STAKES

1) Canford Cliffs and Toronado
2) Petite Etoile and Humble Duty
3) The first was called Noalcoholic and the second was called Alcohol Free
4) B – Chelsea
5) Here Comes When and Lightning Spear
6) Soviet Star and Soviet Song
7) C – Troon
8) A – Ron Hutchinson
9) B – Pascal
10) Gordon Richards

Quiz No. 59 – HISTORIC HANDICAPS No. 1 – THE AYR GOLD CUP

1) B – Dazzle
2) Redford and Brando
3) Louis the Pious

4) Fonthill Road
5) Ian Balding and Karl Burke
6) Highland Colori
7) Coastal Bluff
8) Dandy Nicholls and Kevin Ryan
9) 2018
10) Bielsa

Quiz No. 60 – HISTORIC HANDICAPS No. 2 – THE CAMBRIDGESHIRE

1) John Gosden
2) 100-1
3) Prince de Galles
4) Baronet
5) A – Jupiter
6) D – Mark Prescott
7) John Lowe
8) John Reid
9) Rambo's Hall
10) Marcus Tregoning

Quiz No. 61 – HISTORIC HANDICAPS No. 3 – THE CESAREWITCH

1) Doug and Eph Smith
2) Big Easy
3) Lester Piggott
4) Jason Watson and Silvestre de Sousa
5) Brooke Sanders and Mary Reveley
6) Willie Mullins
7) Go South
8) Mark Johnston
9) Never Can Tell
10) Vintage Crop

Quiz No. 62 – HISTORIC HANDICAPS No. 4 – THE CHESTER CUP

1) Making Miracles
2) Bulwark, Address Unknown, Suegioo and Magic Circle
3) Prescription
4) Anak Pecan
5) Rainbow High
6) Travelling Light
7) David Yates
8) Charlotte's Choice and Morgan's Choice
9) Arapahos
10) B – Frankie Durr

Quiz No. 63 – HISTORIC HANDICAPS No. 5 – THE EBOR

1) Gladness
2) D – Joe Sime
3) Ernie Johnson and Frankie Durr
4) Swinburn
5) Amanda Perrett, Jane Chapple-Hyam and Lady Jane Cecil
6) Sea Pigeon
7) Henry Cecil
8) Luca Cumani
9) Jamie Spencer
10) Newbury

Quiz No. 64 – HISTORIC HANDICAPS No. 6 – THE LINCOLN

1) Paul Cole
2) Vandervelde
3) William Haggas

4) Right Wing
5) A – Scobie Breasley
6) Alex Greaves
7) They used the names of the winners from 1926 to 1937 in their 'Totopoly' boardgame
8) D – Ob
9) Dermot Weld
10) Barry Hills, who was working for John Oxley, financed his career as a trainer with his winnings from the race

Quiz No. 65 – HISTORIC HANDICAPS No. 7 – THE NORTHUMBERLAND PLATE

1) The Pitman's Derby
2) Angel Gabrial
3) Kevin Darley
4) Underhand
5) Tominator
6) George Chaloner and George Baker
7) Paul Cole and James Fanshawe
8) Toldo
9) Willie Carson
10) Tug of War

Quiz No. 66 – HISTORIC HANDICAPS No. 8 – THE PORTLAND

1) Muthmir
2) Oxted
3) Quinn – Jimmy and John
4) Out After Dark
5) Hogmaneigh
6) Charlie Hills
7) David Marnane, David Barron and David O'Meara
8) Kevin Darley
9) The 1990s
10) Halmahera and Kevin Ryan

Quiz No. 67 – HISTORIC HANDICAPS No. 9 – THE ROYAL HUNT CUP

1) Zhui Feng
2) 50-1
3) Colour Sergeant
4) Face North
5) They were the only seven-year-old winners
6) Jeremy Noseda
7) B – John Dunlop
8) D – Johnny Murtagh
9) It was the only horse to win it after finishing second the year before
10) Clive Cox

Quiz No. 68 – HISTORIC HANDICAPS No. 10 – THE STEWARDS CUP

1) Longbow
2) Richard Hannon Senior
3) Gift Horse and Gifted Master
4) Paul Cook
5) B – Monet
6) Rotherfield Greys
7) Dandy Nicholls
8) A – Roger Charlton
9) Easterby – Tim and Mick
10) Green Ruby

Quiz No. 69 – HISTORIC HANDICAPS No. 11 – THE VICTORIA CUP

1) A – Reg Akehurst

2) Josephine Gordon and Hayley Turner
3) Willie Carson
4) Chivalry
5) Lomax
6) C – Lingfield Park
7) A – The Eclipse
8) Richard Quinn
9) Barry, John, Michael and Richard Hills
10) Lincoln

Quiz No. 70 – HISTORIC HANDICAPS No. 12 – THE WOKINGHAM

1) Wokingham
2) They were the horses involved in the only dead-heat in the race in 2003
3) Johnny Murtagh
4) Iffraaj
5) John and Ed Dunlop
6) Outback Traveller and Out Do
7) York Glory
8) Reg and Jon Akehurst – father and son
9) D – Whistler's Daughter
10) America

Quiz No. 71 – HORSES FOR COURSES

1) Piper's Note
2) Rapid Lad
3) Supermaster
4) Plum Pudding
5) Further Flight
6) Pour La Victoire
7) Tingle Creek
8) Mr. Wolf
9) Certain Justice
10) Perucio

Quiz No. 72 – THE IRISH DERBY

1) B – Santa Claus
2) Hurricane Run and Dylan Thomas
3) Santiago
4) Mick Kinane, Kieren Fallon, Seamie Heffernan and Johnny Murtagh
5) Andre Fabre, John Gosden and Charlie Appleby
6) Balanchine
7) Michael Stoute, Luca Cumani, John Oxx and Dermot Weld
8) B – Thirteen of Diamonds
9) Lester Piggott
10) A – Australia at 1-8

Quiz No. 73 – THE JOCKEYS' CHAMPIONSHIP – THE FLAT

1) Paul Hanagan and Richard Hughes
2) 2009
3) Joe Mercer, Michael Roberts and Kevin Darley
4) Fred Archer
5) D – Gordon Richards
6) A – Flatman
7) False – Gordon Richards won it in the 1920s, 1930s, 1940s and 1950s
8) Otto Madden in 1898 and Oisin Murphy in 2019 and 2020
9) Frankie Dettori and Kieren Fallon
10) Jamie Spencer and Seb Sanders

Quiz No. 74 – THE JOCKEYS' CHAMPIONSHIP – THE JUMPS

1) He won it as an amateur and a professional jockey

2) B – 20
3) C – Fred Rimell
4) C – Peter Scudamore
5) C – Fred Rees
6) D – Mason
7) Peter Scudamore
8) Billy Stott and Gerry Wilson
9) Barry
10) True

Quiz No. 75 – MISSING INGREDIENTS – No. 1 – HORSES

1) Saxon Warrior
2) Harzand
3) Bosra Sham
4) Ouija Board
5) Bollin Eric
6) Comply or Die
7) Collier Bay
8) Looks Like Trouble
9) Finian's Rainbow
10) Florida Pearl

Quiz No. 76 – MISSING INGREDIENTS – No. 2 – TRAINERS

1) Jeremy Tree
2) Marcus Tregoning
3) Ben Hanbury
4) Michael Jarvis
5) Jeremy Noseda
6) Dr. Richard Newland
7) Martin Pipe
8) Mark Bradstock
9) Colm Murphy
10) Venetia Williams

Quiz No. 77 – MISSING INGREDIENTS – No. 3 – JOCKEYS

1) Michael Roberts
2) Padraig Beggy
3) CP Lemaire
4) Ryan Moore
5) Jimmy Fortune
6) Richard Guest
7) Philip Carberry
8) Conor O'Dwyer
9) Richard Johnson
10) Adrian Maguire

Quiz No. 78 – MISSING INGREDIENTS – No. 4 – THE YEAR

1) 2002
2) 1984
3) 2013
4) 1985
5) 2010
6) 2000
7) 2006
8) 1963
9) 2015
10) 2016

Quiz No. 79 – MISSING WORDS

1) Prince

2) Blue
3) Court
4) Moon
5) Palace
6) High
7) Fairy
8) Sea
9) Snow
10) Charlie

Quiz No. 80 – 'OH I DO LIKE TO BE BESIDE THE SEASIDE' BRIGHTON RACES

1) Steve Cauthen
2) Jack Berry
3) Park Top
4) The Stewards' Cup
5) Lester Piggott
6) Lord Huntingdon – aka Willie Hastings – Bass
7) They were attacked by a dog
8) Sheikh Mohammed
9) Hethersett
10) A – Neil Callan

Quiz No. 81 – OWNERS – FLAT RACING

1) The Queen
2) The Aga Khan
3) Christopher Tsui
4) Sheikh Mohammed
5) Dr Carlo Vittadini
6) Princess Haya of Jordan and Mrs Jean Hislop
7) Robert Sangster
8) Nelson Bunker-Hunt
9) Khalid Abdulla
10) (a) Charles Engelhard (b) Lord Howard de Walden (c) Louis Freedman (d) Hamdan Al Maktoum

Quiz No. 82 – OWNERS – JUMPS RACING

1) B – Furlong
2) Ten Up
3) Hennessy
4) Freddie Starr
5) Hedgehunter, Ballabriggs and Many Clouds
6) A – August
7) Specify
8) Tooth
9) Mrs C Swallow and Mrs J Samuel
10) Nine

Quiz No. 83 – PIGGOTT PUZZLERS

1) B – Elland Road
2) B – Private Eye
3) B – Money for Nothing
4) B – 6-1
5) B – Magnum Force
6) C – Nixon
7) C – Mott the Hoople
8) D – Billy Fury
9) D – Pisces
10) A – Custer

Quiz No. 84 – POT LUCK

1) Lad
2) The Irish Derby – Dylan Thomas, Australia and Jack Hobbs
3) Moore – George and Ryan
4) Lorenzaccio and Sassafras
5) 1973
6) Might Bite
7) Cottage
8) Johnson – Ernie and Richard, and Dwyer – Martin and Mark
9) One For Arthur
10) Cape Byron

Quiz No. 85 – QUOTES

1) A – Basil Briscoe on Golden Miller
2) D – Ronnie Wood
3) C – Dave Nevison
4) A – Lady Beaverbrook
5) C – Robin Cook
6) D – David Elsworth
7) D – Harry Redknapp
8) A – Julian Wilson
9) B – John Francome
10) D – Jonjo O'Neill

Quiz No. 86 – SECONDS, ANYONE?

1) Excelebration
2) Shoemaker
3) Youmzain
4) Deano's Beeno
5) Theatreworld and My Tent Or Yours
6) D – Yellow Jack
7) Flintshire
8) Growl
9) Waffle
10) Tastahil

Quiz No. 87 – SEQUENCES

1) Harzand
2) Sleepytime
3) Hurricane Fly
4) Mister Baileys
5) Snow Fairy
6) Imperial Commander
7) Galileo Chrome
8) Adayar
9) Put The Kettle On
10) Workforce

Quiz No. 88 – 'SORRY MATE, IT'S NOT HERE THIS YEAR!'

1) Doncaster
2) York
3) Newbury
4) Windsor
5) Newmarket
6) Nottingham
7) Sandown
8) Pontefract
9) Gatwick
10) Thirsk

Quiz No. 89 – TOP JUMPS RACES – A SELECTION
No. 1 – THE CHARLIE HALL

1) One Man and Ollie Magern
2) B – Deep Purple
3) Michael and Monica Dickinson, and Robert Earnshaw and Graham Bradley
4) D – Nigel Twiston-Davies
5) Graham Lee and Paul Moloney
6) D – Set Point
7) Frances Crowley and Rebecca Curtis
8) Davy Lad and Burrough Hill Lad
9) D – Goolagong
10) Silviniaco Conti and Cue Card

Quiz No. 90 – TOP JUMPS RACES – A SELECTION
No. 2 – THE FIGHTING FIFTH HURDLE

1) Comedy of Errors
2) Birds Nest
3) Epatante and Not So Sleepy
4) Dato Star
5) Monica Dickinson
6) Mary Reveley and Jessica Harrington
7) Irving
8) The French Furze
9) Harchibald
10) B – David Elsworth

Quiz No. 91 – TOP JUMPS RACES – A SELECTION
No. 3 – THE HENNESSY – (NOW THE LADBROKES TROPHY)

1) B – Cheltenham
2) Cloth Cap and Cloudy Glen
3) Mandarin
4) Bregawn, Burrough Hill Lad and Bobs Worth
5) Native River
6) April Seventh
7) Many Clouds
8) Spanish Steps
9) Theatre Guide and Fiddlerontheroof
10) De Rasher Counter

Quiz No. 92 – TOP JUMPS RACES – A SELECTION
No. 4 – THE IMPERIAL CUP

1) Secret Service
2) Lanzarote
3) Langer Dan
4) Barney Curley
5) They all won a bonus prize for going on to win at the Cheltenham Festival that season
6) B – Nine
7) Timmy Murphy and AP McCoy
8) They were all trained by women – Dina Smith, Lucy Wadham and Laura Mongan
9) True
10) A – Anglesey

Quiz No. 93 – TOP JUMPS RACES – A SELECTION
No. 5 – THE IRISH GRAND NATIONAL

1) D – Porridge
2) Dreaper – Tom and Jim
3) Thunder and Roses
4) Arkle and Desert Orchid
5) Tied Cottage

6) Organisedconfusion
7) Ger Fox and Mouse Morris
8) Jodami and Cool Dawn
9) C – Rust Never Sleeps
10) The trainer and jockey were the same man – Aubrey Hastings

Quiz No. 94 – TOP JUMPS RACES – A SELECTION
No. 6 – THE LONG WALK HURDLE

1) Punchestowns and Thistlecrack
2) B – Richard Johnson
3) Paisley Park
4) Kelso Chant
5) John Francome and Fred Winter
6) John Cherry
7) Royal Athlete
8) Lanzarote
9) AP McCoy at Windsor
10) Reg Hollinshead

Quiz No. 95 – TOP JUMPS RACES – A SELECTION
No. 7 – THE SCOTTISH GRAND NATIONAL

1) Bogside
2) Red Rum in 1974
3) Take Control
4) Joe – in Joe's Edge and Joe Farrell
5) Aurora's Encore
6) Paris Pike
7) Earth Summit
8) Vicente
9) Full of Oats
10) Wayward Prince

Quiz No. 96 – TOP JUMPS RACES – A SELECTION
No. 8 – THE TRIUMPH HURDLE

1) Tiger Roll
2) Kribensis and Katchit
3) Nicky Henderson
4) Snow Drop
5) B - Penzance
6) Persian War
7) C – Lester Piggott
8) Quilixios
9) Barry Geraghty
10) Countrywide Flame

Quiz No. 97 – TOP JUMPS RACES – A SELECTION
No. 9 – THE WELSH GRAND NATIONAL

1) Mountainous
2) Venetia, Evan and Christian Williams
3) Yala Enkl
4) Halcon Genelardais
5) Martin Pipe
6) Richard Johnson
7) Carl Llewellyn and Ruby Walsh
8) Burrough Hill Lad and Cool Ground
9) Synchronised and Native River
10) Rag Trade, Corbiere and Earth Summit

Quiz No. 98 – TOP JUMPS RACES – A SELECTION
No. 10 – THE WHITBREAD GOLD CUP

1) Arkle
2) Nicky Henderson
3) Diamond Edge
4) D – Newcastle
5) Ad Hoc
6) Alan King
7) Taxidermist
8) Monkerhostin
9) B – 40-1
10) A) Neville Crump

Quiz No. 99 – WHAT WERE THE ODDS ON THAT?

1) C – 95-40
2) 40-85
3) Evens and Odds
4) D – 20-1
5) B – 7-2
6) Sir Ivor, Shergar and Camelot
7) 100-30
8) C – Even Money
9) Six – between 2004 and 2009
10) 16-1 was the longest and 1-2 was the shortest

Quiz No. 100 – WILD CARD

1) Hughes – Brian and Richard
2) Churchill
3) Detroit
4) Harry and Geoff Wragg, and Vincent and David O'Brien
5) Highland Wedding and Eddie Harty
6) Celtic Shot
7) April The Fifth
8) Nicholls – Dandy and Paul
9) Three Troikas
10) Winter